SPACE AGE INDIANS

Other Books by Ardy Sixkiller Clarke

Encounters with Star People: Untold Stories of American Indians

Sky People: Untold Stories of Alien Encounters in Mesoamerica

More Encounters with Star People: Urban American Indians Tell Their Stories

SPACE AGE INDIANS:

THEIR ENCOUNTERS WITH THE BLUE MEN, REPTILIANS, AND OTHER STAR PEOPLE

ARDY SIXKILLER CLARKE

ANOMALIST BOOKS
*San Antonio * Charlottesville*

An Original Publication of ANOMALIST BOOKS
**Space Age Indians: Their Encounters with the Blue Men,
Reptilians, and Other Star People**
Copyright 2019 by Ardy Sixkiller Clarke
ISBN: 978-1-949501-00-1

Cover Art/Photo Credit: South Dakota Stormy Skies by Lisa
Woodburn/iStock; Rocket Start by Alexyz3d/iStock
Book Design: Seale Studios

For information about the publisher, go to AnomalistBooks.com,
or write to:
Anomalist Books, 5150 Broadway #108, San Antonio, TX 78209

TABLE OF CONTENTS

FOR KIP

"I like my computer,
I'm an Indian of the future,
Space Age Indian, I won't be left behind,
Space Age Indian, I'm changing with the times."

"Space Age Indian,"
Tiger Tiger

A NOTE FROM THE AUTHOR

Some historians date the beginning of the Space Age back to 1926 when Robert H. Goddard launched the first liquid fuel rocket. In June 1944, a German V2 rocket became the first man-made object to enter space. Despite these ventures, most historians trace the beginning of the space age to 1957, when the Soviet Union launched Sputnik, the world's first artificial satellite, and they view its end occurring on July 20, 1969, when Apollo 11 astronauts Neil Armstrong and Buzz Aldrin landed their module on the moon and walked on the lunar surface. Since the end of the Apollo program in 1972, the public's interest in manned space exploration has waned, and the public in general has moved on to other things.

Just as the span of years defined as the space age varies, so does the lifespan of the interviewees in this book, but they share one thing in common: *They lived to see two indigenous astronauts launched into space.* In 2002, Commander John Herrington, an enrolled Chickasaw member, was launched into space. He was followed in 2009 by José Hernández, a California native from the Purépecha Indian tribe in the northwestern region of the Mexican state of Michoacán. While little attention has been paid to the indigenous roots of these two astronauts, they both have served as an inspiration to Amerindian youth.

It's hard to believe that during this same period I've collected more than four thousand stories about Star People. Since my first book, *Encounters with Star People*, I have collected one thousand eight hundred and sixty-eight additional stories. There are so many more stories waiting to be recorded, but I would need two lifetimes to complete the task. Recording these accounts became akin to breathing to me. It was nothing I planned; it just became something I had to do.

Although all the accounts hold an important place in my heart, in this book I was especially interested in the stories from individuals who had grown up during the age of space exploration. This group is sometimes referred to by the elders as the Space-Age Indians and immortalized in song by the Miccosukee rock and roll duo, Tiger Tiger. I wanted to learn if their perceptions and experiences were different from those of their elders. I wanted to determine if the Cold War, the space race, or pop culture had affected their recollection of encounters. So I limited my selection of stories to individuals in their teens to early seventies, who had lived in the space age. All of the interviewees were users of computers, the internet, or social media.

I organized the narratives into three major categories: Encounters with Blue Men, Encounters with Reptilians and Insectoids, and Encounters with Other Star People. While these alien races have appeared in my other three books, they have not been a focus of my work. Due to the extraordinary nature of these encounters, I have decided that it is time to share with my readers these amazing and sometimes bizarre accounts.

As you take this journey with me, please keep in mind that I was open to the experiences of individuals who described beings who weren't like us and were superior to us both intellectually and physically. I learned about space travelers who had extraordinary abilities and, in some cases, had performed miracles. I discovered that there were several races of space visitors, some of whom were benevolent while others were malevolent. I also learned that some alien species had an almost-human concern for animals.

Often the most important things I found were revealed unexpectedly, though they weren't always obvious. Anthropologists described this sort of insight as "limbic" space where you free yourself to accept a new vision of life and reality different from what you expect. By opening yourself to the significance of the encounters, you are forced to accept the extraordinary variety of the visitations. It's only by doing this that you are able to understand the depth of the encounters.

It is my sincere hope that as you read about the encounters, you too will be willing to enter the limbic state and accept the stories as they are told.

Personally, I have no difficulty in imagining what happened to these individuals. My record of their encounters is as legitimate as the actual occurrence, since all the participants, witnesses, and victims, whether still alive or long dead, are valid and written as they were told to me. As a result, their encounters live through my books and the voices of my readers who retell their stories.

In retelling these encounters, you, the reader, make the encounters a part of the communal knowledge of ufology. The accounts are no longer a symbol of a single life's encounter. They belong to the collectivity and reside in the minds of the people who have heard or read their stories.

Parents will tell their children of the encounters; grandparents their grandchildren. I will tell mine.

Ardy Sixkiller Clarke

SECTION 1

THE BLUE MEN

1. THE BLUE MEN: INTRODUCTION

In UFO literature, the Blue Men are not often discussed. Probably one of the most famous reports of Blue Men comes from Whitley Strieber who described his encounter with beings who had "wide faces, either dark gray or dark blue…with glittering deep-set eyes, pug noses and broad somewhat human mouths."

Robert Morning Sky, a Hopi-Apache speaker, stated the Blue Men or "Blues" had translucent skin and large almond-shaped eyes, and were small in stature. Mary Sutherland reported that, in addition to the four races of humans, there was once a fifth race who dwelled on an unknown continent. This race, the most ancient of all, was blue. They were about seven feet tall and had extremely large heads. They possessed mind control, including the abilities of teleportation, telekinesis, and ESP. One day, they located a planet more suitable to their needs in a far distant solar system and teleported themselves there, disappearing from the face of the Earth.

Blue Otter, a Cherokee elder of the Prophecy Keepers, reported that the Cherokee encountered Blue People when they first came to the land now referred to as the state of Tennessee. According to the legends, when they arrived they discovered well-maintained gardens tilled by a race of blue people who lived underground. They had large eyes and came out at night using the light of the moon. The Cherokees called them the Moon People or the Blue-Skinned People. Throughout the complex cosmology of the Cherokee, elders described a universe where humans shared the world with other, non-human, supernatural peoples. However, the Moon-Eyed People were never described as supernatural but as another race who were physically different from the Cherokee. According to one Cherokee legend, the Moon-Eyed people fought and lost a war against the neighboring Creek nation. Another version of the story claimed the Cherokee waged war against the Moon-Eyed People, driving them from the Cherokee village of Hiwassee, in what is now Murphy, North Carolina.

Others say that the blue-skinned people never disappeared but chose to remain underground. In northern Arkansas, a twelve-man speleological team encountered inhabitants nearly one mile underground. The explorers found a tunnel illuminated by greenish phosphorescence where they met a race of beings who stood seven to eight feet tall and had blue skin. The beings possessed advanced technology and lived in massive underground cities.

In this section, you will read the stories of American Indian veterans. While their ages and the wars spanned several decades, their descriptions of the Blue Men appeared similar. In all cases, the Blue Men demonstrated benevolent actions. In some of the accounts, the Blue Men offered to take the men to a place where there was no war. This theme was not new to me as I had interviewed others who spoke of another world where peace prevailed.

In other cases chosen for this section, you will find stories of healings that ranged from life-saving events to improved vision. Others tell stories of witnessing amazing feats performed by the Blue Men, including the teleportation of an automobile.

2. IRA'S STORY: THE SHINING BLUE MEN AND THE SPACE AGE INDIANS

In December, I traveled to Hawaii to meet with a former interviewee and to connect with some colleagues involved in the Native Hawaiian Charter School movement. While I was there, I learned that an old friend had been admitted to the Veteran's Hospital on the island. Ira, who identified himself as a Dakota Sioux and the best tracker in the Vietnam War, had lived on the island since he left the military. He once told me that he saw Hawaii the first time when he was on R&R while in Vietnam, fell in love with the islands, and decided to stay there once he was a civilian. Ira, who was named for a Pima Indian marine immortalized as one of the six marines in the famous photo of the flag raising on Iwo Jima, suffered for years from COPD and emphysema. As a veteran, Ira took a lead role on Oahu in organizing veterans who chose Hawaii as their home. As I entered his room, a broad smile crossed his face as he struggled to sit up in his bed. A nurse quickly came to his rescue, adjusted his pillows, and handed him the control for his bed. After a hug and kiss, I sat down by my friend's side. I had not come to the hospital to hear a story about UFOs, but that is exactly what happened.

"Don't let anyone tell you that your elder years are the best years of your life," Ira said as he struggled to speak. "I never thought my life would end this way."

I held his hand and listened, knowing there were no words that could miraculously cure his condition. He was no longer the cocky, muscular young man I met one night on a beach at Waikiki. His black hair had turned white and hung in thin threads down his chest. His breathing was labored, and even with oxygen I watched as his chest heaved up and down with each breath.

"I saw two of your cousins recently," I said, changing the subject. "I told them I planned to see you, and they send you their love and wish that you'd come home and visit all your relatives on the reservation."

"I plan to go after I die. In fact, I wanted to talk with you about my ashes. I want you to take them home and spread them over Strawberry Hill. You know the place." Before I could respond, the door opened and six elderly men entered the room pushing a trolley with a birthday cake. They launched into the Happy Birthday song. Afterwards, they pulled out a bottle of Jack Daniels and seven shot glasses and toasted Ira's seventy-second birthday. Ira quickly capped the bottle and then hid it safely under his pillows as he introduced me to his comrades in crime.

"I want to introduce you guys to the love of my life," Ira began as he pointed toward me. "I met her one night on a beach where a group of us were partying. She was working at the Moana as a housekeeper on summer break from college, and I was in recovery from our stint in 'Nam. At the time, I didn't know she would go on to be a university professor and a writer. Over the years, she has remained faithful to me and is my only link with my family on the reservation. She also holds the distinction of being the only woman I ever asked to marry me." They all laughed and raised their glasses in my direction. "Of course, she also holds the distinction of being the only woman to say no to my proposal." Again, they raised their glasses and laughed uproariously. Ira looked at me and winked, and for a moment he reminded me of the macho man I met decades ago.

Once the toasts and laughter ended, I looked at the group hovering around Ira's bed. "What are your tribes?" I asked.

Each one identified their tribal affiliation.

"What are the odds that seven American Indian veterans would all be living in Hawaii?" I asked.

"We were all in the same squad in Vietnam," Chester said. "Whether it was intentional or not, only Uncle Sam could answer that. One lieutenant told me that Indians were the best trackers and that's the reason we were detailed to the Recon Unit."

"These men are my brothers. For some of us, it is the only family we've ever had," Clay added. My attention was drawn to Clay. He was the only man in the room who was not dressed in sandals and Bermuda shorts. Born on a reservation in northeastern Montana, he had never adopted the laid-back island fashions worn by the men in Hawaii.

"Once Ira saw Hawaii, he talked all the time about moving to Hawaii," Addison added, looking over his horn-rimmed glasses. "When his tour ended, he told us if we ever needed a place to crash, his door would always be open, and one by one, we all ended up here."

"We had each other's backs in 'Nam and that hasn't changed," Mathias said. "We helped each other through drug addiction, alcoholism, and PTSD. We were best friends in war and best friends in life." I noticed his accent. There was no doubt that he had not lost his southern drawl.

"To the space age Indians and brotherhood," Wilson said, as he poured another round of Jack Daniels and the group toasted each other.

"Who are the space age Indians?" I asked.

"We are!" they replied in unison. I watched as they passed the bottle around again, dumbfounded by the moniker they had chosen for themselves, but made no comment about their revelation.

When the bottle of Jack Daniels was half-empty, the conversation turned to the books I wrote. Chester asked Ira if he had ever shared with me the story of their encounter in Vietnam. When Ira admitted that he had never told me of the event, the group settled around the bed to tell me their story. "This encounter is the reason we call our group the Space Age Indians," Chester explained. Somewhat taken back by his comment, I looked at Ira, who squeezed my hand reassuringly and struggled to speak.

"I'll start at the beginning," Ira said as he paused, removed his oxygen mask, and coughed. After a moment, he continued: "We were a part of a Recon Unit located about twenty miles south of the DMZ. We setup a bivouac in a jungle area that had a few steep hills. One night, we went on a reconnaissance mission into a small valley to the east of our encampment to check out some reported activity. Chester was in command. He was our sergeant." Ira looked at the barrel-chested man who sat on the bed next to him. Chester was the most gregarious of the group, and even today the others deferred to him as their leader.

Chester intervened as Ira struggled to continue speaking. "I sent Ira ahead to scout out the situation. He was the best damn scout in the Marine Corps and kept the rest of us alive." All six men nodded in unison. "I counted on him to keep us safe. When Ira returned, he reported sighting a small band of VC [Viet Cong] on the north hill about two klicks from our position."

"Don't forget the strange blue light," Percy said. I looked at Percy. He was fit and muscular for a man of seventy odd years. A gold chain hung around his neck with a medallion and inscription of unknown origin. Later, he told me that the inscription meant "survivor" in Tày, an indigenous Vietnamese language.

"Yes. The blue light," Chester repeated and looked at the other veterans seated around the room.

Ira continued as a strained look crossed his face. "I didn't know what it was. A huge blue ball hung in the sky about three times the size of the full moon. It was slowly making its way across the sky. I watched it approach the earth, closer and closer, until it rested on the hill across from the VC camp. I heard the excited voices of the VC as it came to rest, but not speaking their language I wasn't sure what they were saying. But I did understand that they seemed as in wonder of it as I was. Shortly after that, I headed back to base to report." Ira paused and reached for his water glass. I picked it up and held it for him as he took several sips.

"When Ira reported the blue light, I discounted it as an anomaly," Chester said. "There were strange things that happened in the jungle at night, but I couldn't shake the feeling that something about this night was different. There were no sounds around us and that made all of us uneasy."

"Usually at night," Mathias interjected, "the jungle reeked with noises and sounds that were sometimes deafening. Despite the unusual situation, Chester ordered us to follow him into the night where the enemy encampment was located. We were no more than a half a klick away from the VC, when a barrage of gunshots pierced the night. Rapid rifle fire, mortar shells, machine gun fire lit up the hillside. Strange thing though, the VC were not firing at us but were directing their fire at the valley below."

"We hunkered down and had a ring-side seat into what appeared as a one-sided battle," Ira said. "The VC fired with abandon at flitting blue reflections moving about in the valley below. We counted three glimmering lights but couldn't make out any forms, although the images appeared to be moving upright and in a methodic fashion. Again and again, the blue images ignored their assault. Finally a beam of light landed squarely in the middle of the enemy. There was a lightning flash and a thunderous boom and we never heard a weapon fire again."

"Did you think the blue entities had taken out the VC encampment?" I asked.

"We didn't know," Chester continued. "I ordered the men to stay hidden and wait out the night and observe. After the explosion on the hillside where the VC were located, we heard no further sounds or firing. While I assumed their encampment had been destroyed, I wanted to approach the camp in daylight. At the same time, Ira was keeping tabs on the blue entities who were roaming the valley floor. Not more than ten minutes passed when Ira alerted me that the blue images had changed direction and were headed toward our position."

"By that time, I recognized the forms to be human-like but encased in this shimmering blue light," Ira interjected. "As Chester ordered us to retreat further into the jungle and away from the direct path of the beings, I turned to lead the team to a safer position when I came face to face with one of them. We both stood and stared at one another. He was a tall being, probably nine feet tall and muscular. I was frozen. I dropped my rifle to the ground and at the same time, he lowered his arm. I knew he wasn't my enemy. I called out to my companions to lower their guns and the seven of us stood in amazement at this giant, shining blue creature that stood before us."

"It was difficult to make out any features," Ira continued, "since the shining light that surrounded him morphed his face. Seconds passed and two other humanoid figures joined him. They stood silently, as though assessing us, then walked passed us and disappeared into the jungle."

"You said they were not your enemies. How did you know that?" I asked.

"I sensed it," Ira replied.

"How did you sense it? Did they speak to you?"

"No, I never heard a voice. I just knew." He looked at the others and they all nodded.

"Moments later," Chester said, "we saw the blue ball that Ira originally saw. It lifted off the hillside and disappeared into the sky."

"We knew we had just encountered star men," Addison said.

"But that's not the end of the story," Ira said, breathlessly as his voice trailed off and he began to cough uncontrollably. When I reached for the nurse's button, Ira held up his hand, and as if by a miracle his coughing stopped. "This story should be told," he said. "I've met other vets who have encountered the blue men, and none of us have ever told our story. I think it's time." The others agreed. Without warning, the nurse entered the room and looked suspiciously at the group. Ira hurried her from his bedside and the conversation continued.

"Along toward dawn, we headed down into the valley," Chester said. "We were still stunned by what we had seen, and every one of us seemed lost in our own thoughts. As Ira headed out in front of us, occasionally returning to assure us the area was clear of VC, we reached the valley floor and began the ascent up the hillside where the enemy encampment had been located."

"Do you remember the smell?" Ira asked. His friends nodded in agreement. "It wasn't the smell of gunpowder. It was an overwhelming smell of hot metal and jungle rot. A cloud of smoke hung over the area, making our eyes sting and our noses run. We gagged and covered our faces."

Suddenly Ira began coughing again. I poured another glass of water from the pitcher and handed it to him. Ira reached behind him and pulled out the Jack Daniels bottle and topped off the water. He took a long drink and smiled. "Just what I needed," he said.

Chester reached for the bottle and filled everyone's shot glasses and continued the story. "The strangest thing about the whole site was there were no bodies. The weapons were there, some melted, others hanging from trees as though flung into the sky. Clustered around the machine gun post were three circles of darkened earth. As we moved around, we found seven more. It was like the enemy soldiers had evaporated and all that was left were discolored circles."

"Dust to dust," Ira commented. His friends nodded and fell silent.

"Do you remember anything else?" I asked

"As we said," Ira continued, "we're not the only ones who saw the blue men. There are other stories out of Vietnam about the blue men. We never reported our experience. We agreed among ourselves to remain silent. The brass would've never believed us anyway."

"Or they'd think we were on the wacky-tabacky," said Wilson, who claimed to be the best-looking member of the group. "But I swear on a stack of Bibles, this happened and it is true."

"Not only blue men were encountered on several occasions by other squads," said Chester. "I'm going to give you the name and address of a friend in another unit who met reptile men in the jungle. His story should be told as well." I handed Chester my notebook, and he wrote the name. I looked at it and decided to stop off in Oklahoma and meet Sherman, the friend of a friend who had a story to tell.

"I know of another vet who encountered the Blue Men," said Addison. "He told me they saved his life. Let me have your notebook. I'll give you another name. You guys remember Ute. We called him Ute because he was a full-blood Ute from Colorado I think. His real name was Alphonse. We felt Ute suited him better. Anyway, he lives on the Big Island and grows coffee. I'll call him and tell him about you. He's a good guy. Unlike us, he married a beautiful Hawaiian girl and had lots of little Utes. If you go see him, I know he will talk to you." He took my notebook and wrote a name, address, and phone number.

"You know, your story is quite unique," I said.

"Bizarre is what it is," Ira said. "But it's true. We were all witnesses to the event." He looked at his companions and they all nodded, and one after another swore the story was told as it happened.

"To me there was irony in the encounter," Chester said.

"What do you mean?" I asked.

"Here we were, the seven of us in this godforsaken part of the world fighting to stay alive while NASA was basking in the glory of putting a man on the moon. That's another reason our name for our group, Space Age Indians, is appropriate. We know more about space than NASA. We have touched space. We know there's life out there; something NASA is still trying to discover."

"And we know something else too," Ira interjected. "Man will never be allowed to move beyond this planet in his present war-mongering mentality. When we encounter an indigenous space race and say, 'We come in peace,' this time we better mean it."

Before leaving the hospital that afternoon, I took the names and email addresses of all of Ira's friends and promised I would keep in touch. At the desk, I spoke with a VA administrator and asked to be notified if Ira's condition changed. I signed a form stating that I would be responsible for taking care of his last arrangements. The next morning as I stepped out of the shower in my hotel room, the phone rang. Ira had passed away in his sleep. He had died exactly seventy-two years on the date of his birth. We had a memorial service on the beach for Ira—his six friends and me. I chose the site of our farewell in the same location where I first met Ira. A Native Hawaiian chant offered up by one of Ira's Native Hawaiian friends pierced the stillness. At midnight we took a dip in the ocean and toasted Ira with shots of Jack Daniels.

On my way home, I carried an urn with Ira's ashes. I planned to take it to North Dakota when the snows melt and spread the ashes on Strawberry Hill, a place where the wild strawberries grow. Deer, antelope, prairie chickens, and rabbits stop by throughout the year. It is a fitting place for the only man to propose to me on a beach in Waikiki.

3. MATHIAS'S STORY: THEY DON'T LIKE WAR

As I was leaving the VA hospital, Mathias called out to me. He invited me to join him for coffee. As we walked to the coffee shop, Mathias, a Choctaw from Philadelphia, Mississippi, explained that he had lied about his age when he joined the Marines and was only sixteen years old when he first set foot on Vietnam. "I'll never forget that day. It was the same day that Neil Armstrong took one giant leap for mankind: July 20, 1969. That was the date. Ironic, isn't it? While the astronauts walked on the moon, I took my first step into hell."

It was not hard to imagine that Mathias, who now walked with a limp and used a cane to steady himself, had managed to enlist in the military at such a young age. Even at his age, he maintained a virile appearance. His white hair set off his bronze skin. His muscular frame was outlined by a t-shirt that proclaimed *U.S. Marines.*

"I was big for my age," he explained. "When I joined, I was six-foot-four and weighed about a hundred-and-ninety pounds. Even though I'd just finished the eighth grade, I looked older. It was easy to fool the recruiters. I didn't have a birth certificate, but that was common for Indians in those days. Most of us were born at home and our births were never recorded."

"What about high school?"

"There was no high school for Choctaws back then. My only choice was to join the military or move to Cherokee. [The Cherokee Qualla Boundary in North Carolina had a high school.] My folks couldn't afford to board me in Cherokee so I joined the Marine Corps. I enlisted for three years. I had no idea what I'd done."

We entered the coffee shop and took a table at the rear of the room. Mathias smiled at the waitress who appeared at our table and called her by name. After she took our order, I watched as Mathias pulled an inhaler out of his pants' pocket and took two long breaths. "My breathing gets bad when I walk," he explained as he dropped the inhaler into his shirt pocket.

"Did you have something to add to Ira's story about the Blue Men?" I asked.

"Not really. I think we covered everything about that night."

"Is there something else you would like to tell me?" I asked.

He nodded and drew a long sigh.

"It happened the night before I was scheduled to leave 'Nam," he began. "All the other guys were drafted, so they only served two years. One by one they shipped out after they served their tour of duty. I was the only one of the seven still in country. The night before I was to leave Vietnam, I was on guard duty. Afterwards I retreated to my bunk wondering if I was going to be able to even leave because all night long I watched VC rockets bombarding the Da Nang airport. Along toward 2 a.m. I heard the dreaded yell, 'INCOMING.' In the mayhem, I started for the door when the blast knocked me backward and I landed several yards away from my tent. When I realized I was out in the open with no protection, I headed for cover. Suddenly I felt myself being propelled forward. I must have lost consciousness. I don't know how long I lay there, but when I regained consciousness, I was in the jungle. I could hear the chaos in camp. Fellow marines were crying in pain and officers were yelling orders." Mathias paused and added sugar to his coffee.

"Did you return to camp?" I asked.

"Not right away. I heard another VC rocket pierce the air. I sat up trying to get my bearings, when suddenly the jungle was ablaze. My leg was searing hot. I was in excruciating pain. At that moment, I doubted I would ever see home again, but just as that thought crossed my mind, the Blue Men appeared. One of them shielded my body as several blasts fell nearby. As I lay there half-conscious, an unusual sense of peace flowed over my body. I knew I would make that plane to Okinawa, and I would leave Vietnam behind."

"How did you know that?"

"I sensed it. I felt it in my soul. I no longer worried."

"What about your wound?"

"Once the bombing stopped, one of the Blue Men came forward and placed his hand over my wound and the pain stopped. As I struggled to my feet, the Blue Men stood and disappeared into the jungle. I knew I would be okay, but I never even got to thank them." He paused and finished off his carrot cake and motioned the waitress for a coffee refill.

"Did you ever get your leg treated?"

"About ten years ago, the docs at the VA removed several pieces of shrapnel. That's the reason I walk with a cane."

"Did the Blue Men talk to you, reassure you that you would be okay?"

"No words were ever exchanged. I just knew in my heart that I would be going home in one piece."

"Can you describe the Blue Men?"

"They were tall, taller than me. Maybe seven or eight feet tall. The one that shielded me from the blasts covered my entire body, and I was a big man back then. Strange thing, I never felt his weight on my body although he was on top of me." He stopped and stared out the window at a couple arguing in the parking lot.

"How do you explain it then?" I asked.

"I don't think the Blue Men are physical beings like humans. They are glowing, shimmering blue lights that appear as human forms. I can't describe their faces because the shimmering blue light concealed their faces. I think they are made up of energy. Perhaps, in their world, they take a physical form, but on Earth they are pure energy. But I believe they don't like war. They are peaceful beings, and in their presence I felt peace and love. I think they chose me to save. There were other marines that died that night, but they saved me."

"Why do you think they chose you?"

"They said they knew me. I believe they knew I was with my friends the night they encountered the VC."

"How do you feel about that?"

"I feel like they are looking out for me. I hope I meet them again. But they only seem to appear when there's danger. Maybe just in war. I don't think they like war."

"Obviously you did make it home." I said.

"Thanks to the Blue Men," Mathias said. "I don't remember much about the trip to the airport. When the plane lifted off there was a cheer that went up inside that plane like you might hear at an NFL football game when your team scores a touchdown. The plane took us to Okinawa where I cleaned up and changed into my traveling uniform. I was supposed to head to Mississippi. Instead I flew to Hawaii and ended up on Ira's doorstep. I knew I had come home."

I saw Mathias last Christmas. He and Addison are now roommates. When I am in Honolulu, I always join the six former marines for their weekly Sunday dinners. They have since made me an honorary member of the Space Age Indians. After dinner, we stroll to the beach, and at the place where we bade Ira farewell, we toast him with a bottle of Jack Daniels. We linger long into the night. Everyone has a story to tell about Ira. When the sun comes up, we walk to a nearby restaurant for breakfast. Sometimes, we stop for a game of checkers with other locals who seem to be a permanent fixture on the beach. I am happy to be with them, these Indian warriors, these Space Age Indians, who manage to live each day to its fullest on the beach at Waikiki. As I watched them flirt with the mini-clad females who stopped by their game, Mathias jokingly pointed out, "We ain't dead yet." They all agreed. I did too.

4. WILSON'S STORY: BROTHERHOOD
KEPT ME ON EARTH

Wilson, whom I had met the day of the buddy reunion in Ira's hospital room, drove me to the funeral home to collect Ira's ashes. During our drive, he admitted that he had added very little to the conversation about the Blue Men, but that he had his own story to tell and wanted to share it in private. He drove to the parking lot of the Waikiki Shell. Except for a sports car, the lot was empty. We climbed out of the car and sat on the hood of his Ford Sedan before he continued.

"What we witnessed in Vietnam changed my life forever. My grandfather used to tell me stories about the stars and the star men. But he never told me about the Blue Men."

"How did it change your life?" I asked.

"If it hadn't been for the interference of the Blue Men, we would have all died that night. We didn't stand a chance. The VC were positioned in such a way, that any movement, a rustle of a leaf, the flight of a bird, anything would have brought the full force of their weapons down on us. We were totally unprepared for their artillery. And yet, we survived."

"Did that bother you?" I asked.

"Hell yes, it bothered me. I wondered if they saved us because we were Christian and the VC weren't. I asked myself if God was on our side and not the VC. I speculated that perhaps we were right and stood for good and the VC didn't. These questions almost drove me crazy. We were in their country. We were the aggressors. The war was wrong and we all knew it."

"Did you find answers to your questions?" I asked.

"I did—in the most amazing way. But it took some time." I

watched this quiet man slide down from the hood of his car and look off toward the sleeping volcano that loomed over Waikiki.

"Do you want to tell me about it?" I asked.

"I found my answer up there," he said as he pointed to Diamond Head. I jumped down from the car and walked beside him. His gaze remained on the volcano. "When I came back from 'Nam, I ended up at Ira's. Keeping with Indian tradition, he took me in. At one time, all of us used Ira's place as home base. We slept on the beach, surfed, and spear-fished. We kept silent about our survival, but we all had the same question: why us? We were all victims of Vietnam, but in a way, victims of our saviors, the Blue Men. While we seldom talked about what happened that night, I seemed to be more questioning of the event."

"So you are saying that the others accepted the event?"

"Yes, or at least more than me. When we talked about it, the general consensus was that the event was a part of our legacy as Indians. The Star People had always interacted with our people. Our ancestors knew them, our grandfathers knew them. They were just looking out for us because we were Indians. They were our ancient kin; a part of our DNA."

"And you? Why did you not accept it like the others?"

"I wasn't sure. Hell, we had all heard star ancestor stories that the ancestors watched over us and protected us. It was easy to transfer that belief to the Blue Men. We knew they came from the stars and they saved us."

"But did you believe it?"

"I remember a story from my grandfather. He told of a whole Cherokee village being saved by beings from the stars. The whole village was literally picked up and transported to another place as aggressors approached. He said the Star People watch out for us. They always have and always will."

"But do you believe the Star People look out for our people?" I asked.

"I do now," he said as he began walking away from the car. I caught up with him and noticed his labored breathing. I urged him to sit down, but he seemed lost in his thoughts. He raised his head toward the sky, closed his eyes as if allowing the sun to warm his face.

"When I first came back, I thought of re-enlisting. It's hard to believe that I even considered such a thing, but all I knew was war and the jungle. Every morning I set out for a walk up Diamond Head. It kept me in shape and away from people. In the afternoons, I looked for work. I finally found a job down on the docks, but it was only part-time, so my journey up Diamond Head was delayed until the late afternoon. I didn't enjoy walking as much since tourists were often walking the trail by that time."

"Were you ever on top of Diamond Head at night?" I asked. "I often imagine what the view must be like."

"That's where I saw the Blue Men," he said.

"Are you saying that you saw them after you were in Vietnam?"

He nodded.

"Will you tell me about it?"

"You are not supposed to stay on Diamond Head after dark. In fact, you aren't even allowed to begin the climb after 4:30 p.m. You can be arrested by the military if you disobey. In the 1900s Diamond Head was a defensive military lookout."

"Obviously it was not operational during the Pearl Harbor attack," I said. He looked at me and shrugged.

"Anyway, since that time, it has become a U.S. Natural Monument. Part of the volcano is closed to the public and today serves as a platform for towers and satellite dishes used by the government."

"Did you go into the forbidden area?" I asked.

He nodded.

"My experience in Vietnam helped me hide from the enemy. I considered the government operations on Diamond Head as the enemy. From my vantage point, I was able to view many things— the beach, the city, and UFOs."

"UFOs?"

"Yes, I saw UFOs. I saw them approach Diamond Head and

disappear. I think they must use a cloaking device of some kind. They disappear so no one sees them, but I saw them. I also saw the Blue Men."

"Did they see you?"

"Yes. They told me to stay away from this place because I was in danger."

"Why?"

"They never told me. But they told me that on that night in Vietnam, they saved us because we were not the aggressor. When I explained that I had many questions, I wanted to know what happened to the VC bodies, and they said they took them. They were safe on another world where there was no war."

"Did you believe them?"

"Yes. They told me they would take me there if I wanted to go. I told them I couldn't leave without my buddies. They said they could not wait and that I must leave this area. That was the end of our conversation."

"Did you leave the area immediately as they asked?"

"I had no choice. Suddenly they came toward me and the shimmering blue light surrounded me. The next thing I knew, I was sitting in my car, parked in that very spot. I think they put me there." He turned and looked at his parked car as we made our way back to it.

"Have you ever told the guys about your encounter?"

"No. I think there are some things best unsaid."

"I don't understand."

"I was tempted to go with the Blue Men, but loyalty and brotherhood kept me on Earth. I couldn't leave the guys that had helped me survive in 'Nam. I know if the situation was reversed, they would not leave me. That was our motto. One for all. I couldn't go."

I see Wilson every time I go to Honolulu. Wilson takes me to the town of Haleiwa to enjoy a shaved ice at the world famous, Matsumoto's. He says he waits until I visit the island to go there. On our drive, we always talk about the Blue Men, but to date, he has not been visited again. He admits that not long after his encounter, he ceased his daily trek up Diamond Head.

5. SADIE'S STORY:
A GIFT FROM THE BLUE MEN

While I was making the final arrangements with the funeral director for Ira's ashes, a woman approached me and introduced herself as Sadie. She explained that she and Ira had been friends over the years and often heard him speak of me. As I listened to her speak fondly of my friend in whispered tones, she abruptly pulled me away from the desk and asked if Ira had ever spoken to me about the Blue Men. Startled by her question, I remained speechless as she nervously spoke about the appearance of the Blue Men in a hospital ward one night. She headed for the exit when the funeral director appeared with a catalog of urns. I caught up with Sadie on the street and invited her for drink. An hour later, I was sitting on a mahogany bench in her backyard surrounded by a small jungle of tropical flowers and fruit trees.

"Thank you for agreeing to visit me at home. I don't like to talk about such things in public. Too many ears."

I watched as the petite, soft-spoken woman poured lemonade into two glasses. Her salt and pepper hair was wound into a bun at the nape of her neck. She had a striking face, sharply chiseled with high cheekbones and small slanted eyes, features from a mixed heritage. Dressed in a Hawaiian print muumuu that fell to her ankles, she moved with the grace of a hula dancer.

"If you don't mind my asking, what is your ethnicity?" I asked.

"Believe it or not, I'm half Navajo. My mother was Korean. My father eventually brought us to Arizona when I was three, but mama hated the desert. She finally left the day I graduated from high school. I hung around the rez for a couple of years and enrolled in the pre-nursing program at the tribal college. But I was a Daddy's girl and joined the military—the following in your father's footsteps scenario. I had two years of nursing school when I enlisted, and Uncle Sam helped me realize my dream. By that time, my mama was living in Hawaii. When I finished my degree, I asked for an assignment on the islands."

She stood and picked a hibiscus flower blooming profusely from an enormous bush. "I guess you're wondering how I knew Ira," she began as she placed the flower behind her ear.

I nodded.

"I was a military nurse for twenty-nine years. When the wounded were sent to Hawaii for rehabilitation therapy, I often took care of them during that period. Ira was a gentle man. That's what made me take notice of him."

"Twenty-nine years is a long time," I said.

"Yes. I'm retired now, but that's how I got to know Ira and his friends. All of them spent time at the hospital." She stopped and smiled. "Ira often spoke about you. He called you the 'love of his life.'" Feeling uncomfortable about her comment, I attempted to explain my relationship with Ira.

"We were barely out of our teens when we met," I explained. "We were following different paths; our connection was being Indian. Over the years, we remained friends for that same reason. That's what we do. Indians always look out for each other. I think Ira used me to avoid any commitment to women in his life."

She smiled and shook her head. "It was more than that for Ira." Sadie stood and picked up a cat that had wandered into her backyard. "Ira gave me this cat," she said as she sat down, still holding the cat. "He found her somewhere downtown in a garbage bin."

"At the funeral home," I said, "you spoke of the Blue Men. I write books about encounters with star people. Ira told me they came from the stars. What can you tell me about them?"

"Over the years, I heard dozens of stories from Vietnam vets about the Blue Men. Ira and his Space Age Indians, as he liked to call their group, told me about their encounter, but there were others, many others." She paused and refilled my glass with lemonade. A cool breeze filled the air with the scent of ginger.

"Did you ever see the Blue Men?" I asked.

"Yes, and I'll never forget it. It was in the hospital. It was late at night when everyone was asleep but me," Sadie said. "No one wanted the night shift. It was at night when the crying began. It was at night, when the suicide attempts occurred."

"What happened the night you saw the Blue Men?" I asked.

"It was shortly after midnight. I know the time because, every hour, I made my rounds in the wards, checking on each patient to make sure everything was okay. But this one particular night, when I entered the ward, I saw a light, a strange light."

"Can you describe it?" I asked.

"The whole room was washed in light, a faint, blue light. I scanned the room, but couldn't find the source. When I stepped inside the light, I felt a strange sensation. I remember walking down the aisle of the ward. All my patients appeared to be asleep. I saw nothing unusual until I came to Owen Marks' bed."

"Who was Owen Marks?" I asked.

"A vet who was struggling with living. He lost both his legs in Vietnam and had attempted suicide twice. When I reached his bed, Owen was missing. I panicked. I looked under the bed thinking he might have fallen out in his sleep, and that's when I saw him."

"Owen?" I asked.

"The Blue Men and Owen. Owen was in the corner of the room and on each side of him was a Blue Man. They were just as Ira described them. Huge entities, twice the size of Owen. They had a human form, but there was a luminous glow around them that made their image vague and indistinct."

"What were they doing?"

"Sitting there. It appeared as though they were embracing Owen, almost cradling him like an infant. The shimmering light about them distorted the scene and blinded me. It was difficult to be sure of what I saw. It could have been my imagination, but that's what it looked like."

"Did they see you?" I asked.

"I'm not sure. All the time I was watching them, I had a feeling of peace wash over me. Do you know the feeling of letting all your cares vanish?"

I shook my head.

"It's as though you have no worries, no cares. All the stress of my mother's dementia was gone. All the stress of caring for those poor boys was gone. I was at peace. I can't explain it. It was like God had touched my soul and took away all the pain and anxiety. For some reason, I knew everything was going to be okay."

"How long did you watch the Blue Men?"

"I'm not sure. The night watchman found me asleep at the foot of Owen's bed. I think I must have passed out. When I came to, Owen was sound asleep in his bed."

"Did you talk to him the next day about the Blue Men?"

"He had no memory of being out of bed or of any of the events that occurred. I never asked him about the Blue Men."

"And you're sure of what you saw. Correct?"

"I swear to you, I saw the Blue Men. But there was other evidence."

"What kind of evidence?"

"Owen. Overnight his entire personality changed. He was no longer suicidal. He became a leader in the ward, encouraging others. He even formed a wheelchair basketball team. The hospital psychiatrist was totally puzzled, but I wasn't. I knew what happened. The Blue Men helped him. They work miracles."

"You mentioned that you felt a release of your anxiety and worry. Can you tell me about that?"

"I can't explain it, but I no longer worry about everything. I am calm and at peace. It was a gift from the Blue Men." She paused and took a sip of her lemonade. "You know, when the vets told me stories about the appearance of the Blue Men on the battlefield or in dangerous situations, I took it with a grain of salt. I thought they were imaginings brought on by battle fatigue, fear, or drugs. I never once entertained the thought that the Blue Men were real, but I'm here to testify that they do exist and for some reason they seem to appear to men in battle."

"Why do you say that?" I asked

"I was a nurse for a long time. My career brought me into contact with a wide variety of military vets. I've cared for men who fought in Korea, Vietnam, and World War II. I've heard stories about Blue Men from all of them. The Blue Men have been around as long as I have been a nurse."

She paused and stroked her purring cat.

We sat there in silence. Two strangers connected by the friendship of one man. Finally, I broke the stillness that had settled over the scene and asked "Is there anything else you can tell me about the Blue Men?"

Sadie shook her head and refilled my glass of lemonade.

I did not see Sadie again. Three years later, I was in Honolulu on business when I read in the morning paper that Sadie had passed. A featured story told of her death and provided quotes from vets who had known her over the years. Her obituary appeared the next day in the paper and read, "She was preceded in death by her mother, Lee Begay, and her lifelong friend, Ira Red Eagle." It was obvious that she loved Ira. Her final act on Earth had been to declare her feelings. That night after her funeral, I walked to the beach and sat on the shore. I searched the night sky for any sign of the Star Men. I knew that somewhere up there in the vast nothingness of space, Ira and Sadie were together and that thought gave me comfort. Hopefully the Blue Men were looking out for both of them.

6. UTE'S STORY:
THEY KEEP WATCH ON US

Before leaving Hawaii, I took a short plane trip to the Big Island. I rented a car and drove to the Hilo Hawaiian Hotel off Banyan Drive. The next morning, I set off to meet Ute, who lived about fifteen miles from the town of Hilo. When I parked, I saw Ute sitting on a large deck, watching the driveway. He waved and bounded down the steps in my direction. As Addison stated, Ute was a full-blood Ute and a Vietnam veteran. As he approached, I noted that he could have passed for a number of different ethnic identities found on the Hawaiian Islands. He greeted me as an old friend and suggested that we take a walk. As he led me up a path behind his house, two teenage girls stood on the deck watching us disappear. As we climbed the steep hill toward his coffee bushes, he paused and gave me a hand on the slippery hillside. After we reached the top, we sat on a wooden bench and looked out over his domain. He told me it was his favorite place on the island and a place where he liked "to talk story," a common expression in the islands in which people tell stories from the heart.

"I was eighteen when Uncle Sam sent me to 'Nam," Ute began. "Just a boy right out of high school. Uncle Sam had a long arm and could find you anywhere in those days. I didn't want to go and I thought of going to Canada. I had this dream that I would never see Colorado again or my Dad. There was just Dad and me in those days. I had a sister, but she died of pneumonia when she was twelve. My dad died while I was in 'Nam. I didn't find out about it until six weeks later. By that time, the tribe had already buried him. I never went home then and I haven't been back since."

"Addison told me that while you were in Vietnam you

encountered a Blue Man from the stars. Could you tell me about that?" I asked.

"Are you going to tell my story in your books? Addison told me you wrote about UFO encounters in books."

"I might. I have collected hundreds of stories. Some I choose to tell; others I don't. It depends on a number of things."

"Such as?"

"Whether I believe you or not. Whether the story is so compelling that I think my readers would like to read about it. Whether I can disguise your identity and the place where you live so that no one will ever find you. Just a number of things."

"And you never tell anyone about who told you?" Ute asked.

"Never."

"I would like to read your books before I make a decision. If you've written them to my satisfaction, then I will allow you to print it. Otherwise, this story is between you and me. I don't trust the government. If I tell this story to you and it's published, they might come after me and my wife and kids. So I have to be careful. Do you understand?"

"Yes. You have my word. I will never print your story without your permission."

Ute got up and walked to a small shack located near the wooden bench where we were sitting. When he opened the door, I saw a small refrigerator. He opened it and held up two bottles.

"What will it be—pineapple or guava?" he said. When I told him I preferred pineapple, he closed the refrigerator door and walked back to the bench. He opened the pineapple drink and handed it to me.

"Uncle Sam lied to Americans during the war. I was a part of several units sent to Cambodia. The Cambodians, who claimed neutrality during the war, were not neutral. They allowed the Viet Cong to establish bases and move back and forth across their borders. The year was 1970, and with Nixon's election the US was shifting its position of winning the war to one they called Vietnamization, which was to shore up the Vietnamese government and eliminate the border threat from Cambodia. Of course, we know how that turned out. Nixon claimed it was the South Vietnamese army that was invading Cambodia, but the truth was, we were right there with them." He paused and took a long drink from the bottle of guava juice.

"I understand how you must feel," I said. "I had a brother and uncle in Vietnam. But I heard that you have a story about the Blue Men. Can you tell me about it?"

He nodded and took another drink.

"Our plan was to invade a territory called Parrot's Beak. I don't know why it was called that. I never saw a parrot that day. The VC took us on in full battle. Soldiers were falling all around me. It was probably an hour into the battle before I suddenly realized I was separated from my squad. I was alone."

"What do you mean, you were alone?" I asked.

"None of the men who entered into the invasion with me were standing. They were all dead, dying, or in retreat. I remember finding a large tree. I sat down, my back leaning into it, and I cried. I knew that my dream of never returning to Colorado had come true. I was going to die. There was no escape."

"But that belief must have changed. You're here. What happened?"

"I remember standing and throwing my weapon away. I had killed my last man. If I was going to die, I decided that I wasn't going to be the aggressor. I was going to die without a weapon."

"But you lived. How did you manage to get out of Parrot's Beak?" I asked.

"It was the Blue Men. They saved me."

"How?"

"I fell to the ground in prayer. I asked Jesus to look upon me favorably. I asked him to forgive me for my sins and especially for killing the VC. As I prayed, a light engulfed me and the next thing I knew, I was floating upward through the sky."

"Were you aware that you were being taken away from the battle?"

"No. When the light fell upon me, I thought God had come for me and I was dead. I didn't understand I had been taken by the Blue Men."

"When did you realize that?"

"I woke in a clean, cool room. There were blue lights, a hazy mist, and I was no longer dirty, hot and sweaty. My combat fatigues were clean. I felt fresh and energized. I sat up from a metal table in the room, but I was still disoriented. I had no idea where I was or how I got there. I walked around the room, and I decided I was in heaven, maybe in a holding room, and God was going to judge my fate."

"When did you realize that it was not God, but the Blue Men?" I asked.

"I'm not sure how long I was in the room. I think time must be different in space. It could have been five minutes or five hours for all I know. But as time passed, a tall, blue spirit man entered. I say he was a blue man, but it was hard to make out his characteristics. He appeared luminous but blue. His whole body shimmered. Later he explained to me that their bodies in their natural form were not solid, but they were beings of light. He said they could move back and forth between light and solid material, but it was tedious and for most part they did not take a solid form because people were more alarmed by a solid blue man."

"Did they tell you why they had taken you?"

"To save me. They had been observing the battle and saw me prostrate on the ground, praying, and decided I was worth saving. I'm still waiting to find out what made me worthy when dozens of others died."

"How long did you stay with the Blue Men?" I asked.

"For several days earth time. When the invasion was over and the remaining troops were retreating, I was taken to a safe place where I could join other combat troops unnoticed. When we returned to base, I discovered I was the only one from my squad to survive. That was a tough thing to deal with. I was sent for R&R, and I ended up in Hawaii. I was on the beach in Waikiki one night when I met two Hawaiian girls. They were sisters. They took me home with them, and I met the rest of their family. It was the first time since I was drafted that I felt like I had a home. When I got out of the military, I returned to Hawaii and married the oldest one. We are still together and have six beautiful children. I am blessed. All because of the Blue Men."

"While you were on board their spacecraft, did you learn anything?" I asked.

"I learned that their civilization is more than a million years older than ours. Once they lived in a solid, material form, but over time they learned how to turn their bodies into energy without destroying their soul."

"Soul? What does that mean?" I asked.

"Well now, I am putting my own assumptions on them. I guess it was their soul. They were able to function as beings anyway, but maybe it was not their soul. Anyway, being able to become light beings allowed them to ease the population problem until they could find other worlds where their people could spread out and live."

"Are you saying they told you their planet was overpopulated?"

"Yes. So once they found a way of turning them into light energy, their scientists, leaders, and people of knowledge became light entities."

"And the others?"

"The workers stayed as solid, material objects for a time. Today the light beings and the solid beings live together peacefully. There is no intermarriage between them but a mutual respect for one another. The light beings never age. They can live forever, but they do occasionally become solid beings so they can experience the real world."

"Did they ever become solid in front of you?"

"Only one. He was my caretaker. He felt it would make me more comfortable."

"Can you describe him?"

"As I said, they were giant men. Eight feet tall or taller. Their skin was blue, which they attributed to the atmosphere on their planet. They had perfect human features otherwise. Their civilization has spread out to two other planets in their part of the universe. On one of the planets, the people ceased being blue over time. They have also recorded diminished growth in their offspring."

"Did they take you to their planet?" I asked.

"No, we stayed above the Earth. They had instruments to magnify different places on Earth. That's how they observe what's going on. They don't believe in aggression. They're a peaceful race, and then they use their advanced knowledge and skills to defend themselves peacefully."

"How?"

"Mind control and by removing subjects to a different setting."

"Did you observe any human qualities in the Blue Men?"

"If you mean emotions, I didn't see much. It was obvious that they were compassionate in that they saved me, but I saw no such thing as laughter, joking, sadness, or happiness. They were stoic, all business."

"How did they communicate?"

"In light form, they used telepathy—that was a new word for me—but I learned it was thinking thoughts and responding in thoughts. But when he was in a solid form, my caretaker spoke as you and I spoke. He said few of his people spoke as you and I spoke. Over time, evolution had changed them, and they no longer had to speak."

"What did you think about that?" I asked.

"I told him I wasn't sure I would like to live in a world where people could read my thoughts. He told me that it eliminated needless thinking. People learned only to think and speak when necessary. They learned to keep thoughts blank."

"Did you ask him what effect that had on his people?"

"I asked him if the loss of thoughts and speech impacted his people and he said that it had stifled creativity. As I understand it, they have now corrected that problem."

"How did they do that?" I asked.

"When a child is born to a solid couple, they remove children at the age of two who demonstrate exceptional intelligence. They allow those children to live in a special colony."

"Colony?"

"That's the word he used, but it seemed to mean in an area removed from others. There they are free to dream without their peers knowing their thoughts. These are the future scientists and people of knowledge. Eventually they too become figures of life and help the others in developing new technologies."

"Can you think of anything else they told you?"

"One other thing. They still have babies like we do, but only the solid couples."

"Did he tell you what happens to the other babies that don't meet their intellectual specifications?"

"He said they become workers."

"And who are the workers?" I asked.

"They are the specials. They build the cities and help modernize the new planets. They are taken care of spiritually by the light people and according to him are very happy in their role."

"Has your encounter with the Blue Men changed your life in any way, other than the obvious."

"They saved me, but then I wonder if it was my fate all along and I would have lived without their interference. The fact that I never returned home to Colorado does not mean they had anything to do with it. I fell in love, and the Big Island is my home until the big one blows and sinks it into the sea. But there is one thing: I am a walking example of a man who knows the truth about life in outer space. The Blue Men exist, just as you and I. They keep a watch on Earth and they tell me, if we choose to destroy ourselves, they will let that happen. But, in such a case, if I so choose, they will come for me and my family and take us to another place."

"Do you believe that?" I asked.

"I believe they have that much power. I'm not sure I will go with them. Earth is my home. I can't imagine that I would ever leave Mother Earth. She sustains me by allowing me to support my family, growing coffee in the rich soil on our small twenty-acre farm, and so far I can't think of any place else I would like to live."

"Is there anything else you would like to share with me?" I asked.

"I have a reference for you. I have a friend who was also in 'Nam. Besides Addison and his buddies, there were others who saw the Blue Men."

"Do you have any idea why so many Vietnam veterans saw UFOs during the war?" I asked.

"I've thought about that. I think if you could take a survey of Vietnam veterans, you'd find that probably as many as five out of ten saw UFOs or had direct encounters with aliens. While the stories vary and can seem outrageous at times, I believe their stories. It was a war of the elites fought by the poor. The rich got richer off of Vietnam. The poor got poorer. We came home drug addicted, alcoholic, and mentally ill—all so the fat cats could count their money. Don't ever think that war is fought for democracy. It is to promote capitalism, open up new markets, and subject others to the Ronald McDonald way of life."

After spending all morning with Ute, I had lunch with him and his family. His daughters drilled me with countless questions about Montana, the university, and my lifestyle. They had seen snow twice at the volcano, but they couldn't imagine a world covered with snow for months.

Ute read my books and called me one night to tell me how he appreciated the way I told the stories of his Native brothers and gave me permission to tell his story. Every time I go to the Big Island, I stop and spend a day with Ute and his wife, Laki, and their daughters, Kahi and Lani. His business is doing great and his coffee brand has grown in popularity. One of my pantry shelves hold bags of his special brand. Ute tells me he has yet to see the Blue Men again, but he is not expecting them, unless Armageddon comes.

7. MELE'S STORY: I SAW THE EARTH FROM SPACE

Mele, who admitted to being a drug addict while in Vietnam, underwent treatment when he was stationed in Hawaii after a two-year stint in Vietnam. He decided to make Hawaii his home once discharged from the military. A Chickasaw Indian by birth, Mele preferred the ethnic diversity of Hawaii over his home state, Georgia While he also admitted to being involved in the production of marijuana on a small scale when he first left the military, he attributed his sobriety to his Japanese-Hawaiian wife who supported him while he earned a degree in astronomy. He welcomed my visit when I contacted him about telling his story.

I drove from Hilo to Waimea over the Saddle Road. While Waimea was the center of cattle ranching on the Hawaiian Islands, I met Mele at the 9,200-foot base camp of the astronomical observatory at Mauna Kea. While I lived at nearly 6,000 feet in Montana, I noticed the difference in elevation immediately. As I leaned against the rental car to catch my breath, I saw a man approaching me. He wore Bermuda shorts and a t-shirt with "Save Mauna Kea" emblazoned on the front.

"I'm Mele," he said smiling. "I think you might be looking for me."

"I'm just catching my breath," I said.

"Well, there's about thirty percent less oxygen at this altitude than at sea level. If you need oxygen, I can help. I carry it with me at all times." He turned and showed me a small oxygen unit about the size of a purse. "If it bothers you, we could go to Waimea town."

"I think that might be a good idea," I said as I opened the driver's door and crawled behind the steering wheel. Mele jumped in with me and we slowly descended the volcano. When we arrived in Waimea town, he directed me to Ulu La'au, a nature park in the center of the small town.

"How long have you lived in the islands?" I asked as he guided me along one of the park's trails.

"I'm 71 now. I came here after 'Nam at twenty-one, so fifty years. A half century. I love the islands and particularly this park. While it's state owned, it's leased by the Waimea Outdoor Circle for environmental research, education, and restoration. Their goal has been to remove invasive plant species and replace them with endemic and canoe plants [plants brought to Hawaii by Native Hawaiians in their canoes], along with the endangered and threatened plant species native to Hawaii. It's a place of restoration and anyone who served in Vietnam needs a place of restoration."

"Your friend Ute told me you had a story about the Blue Men. Would you share that story with me?"

"I haven't told this story since I was in 'Nam," he said. "Ute shared with me his encounter and I shared mine. We were brothers in arms in more ways than one. A lot of brothers saw the Blue Men in 'Nam. I've heard many stories. I believe they were a group of alien visitors who found war abhorrent, and they were studying our behavior. Now I must tell you, that's my theory. I have no proof or evidence to support it."

"Tell me about the incident with the Blue Men."

"Did you ever hear of Operation Ranch Hand?" he asked.

I shook my head.

"It was the herbicidal warfare instituted by the military. I was in the Dak Son area when they decided to drop their spray, Agent Orange. That's what they called it. It was deadly stuff. The military killed a lot of their own with Agent Orange." He paused and leaned against a tree. His breathing was labored. "Sorry," he said. "I just need a little rest." We found a bench and sat down.

"Anyway, word came down about the spray. I was bent out of

shape. I knew the brass knew we were in the area, and yet they indiscriminately decided to spray the region. I was looking for a place where I might find some safety when I came upon a cave. The opening was small, but I crawled inside anyway. As I was pushing myself along on my belly, I saw flashes of light further down the cave. I don't know why I did it, but I continued crawling on my belly toward the light. Even when I was doing it, I thought it was a stupid thing to do."

"Can you describe the light?" I asked.

"It was just bright flashes, like you might see if someone was welding in the dark."

"How big was the cave?"

"At the entrance, it was small. I literally was on my belly, pushing myself along with my arms. But about thirty feet inside, the opening became larger and then larger again until I could stand. I'm five feet nine. As I got nearer the light, the flashes increased. I was thinking I had found an opening to one of the VC tunnels. Instead I was in for the surprise of my life."

"Weren't you afraid to explore the cave?"

"I was nineteen. Invincible. I didn't even think. I just wanted to find out what was going on. The cave was winding. In other words, there were a number of turns and bends, but when I came around the third bend, I saw them." He paused and coughed.

"Are you sure you are okay?" I asked.

"I'm sure. Not used to talking so much," he said, grinning at me.

"I have some water." I pulled out a water bottle and handed it to him. He accepted it and took several sips.

"It amazes me what you women carry around with you. No wonder you're in better shape than us guys."

"So when you came around the bend, what did you see?"

"I saw three tall entities. They were surrounded by a blinding blue light. At that time, it hadn't registered with me that they were aliens."

"When did you realize they were Star People?"

"I was trying to conceal myself so I could spy on them. I was still trying to determine who they were and what they were doing. My first thought was that they were wearing strange suits. Then I felt a hand on my shoulder and I almost died of a heart attack: when I turned around, I came face to face with a blue man. Before I could react, he took me by the arm and guided me into an enlarged area. I swear, you could have put a jumbo jet inside the area. It was huge, and in the middle sat a spacecraft."

"Can you describe them?"

"They were big, at least eight feet tall. They were muscular, big muscles on their arms like they were body builders. They made me know they didn't believe in war and weren't there to hurt me or anyone else. While they did not take sides, they felt the pain of both sides. They asked me why I was fighting the other men, and I told them I didn't know except that my government told me to fight."

"How did they react to that?"

"They told me that governments did not control a man's actions on their plane."

"How long did you stay with them?"

"Perhaps an hour in the cave. They offered to take me away with them. When I told them I couldn't go, they offered to remove me to safety. I took them up on that, and they took me on board and placed me in an area free of Agent Orange. It took me several days to find my squad. Everyone thought I was dead. I didn't tell them I was with the Blue Men who saved me from our own military."

"So do I understand that they actually took you onboard their spacecraft?"

"They not only took me onboard, they showed me Earth from space. They told me Earth was too beautiful to be destroyed by war and biological weapons and that I should do more to change it. I discounted their thoughts. I didn't believe I could make a difference."

"Have you changed your mind about that?"

"I believe we can make a change in our family or our

neighborhoods, but I don't think anyone can change the minds of the Washington politicians or brass. They only care about themselves, not us."

"Did the encounter change your life?"

"I got a degree in astronomy. With its high elevation, dry environment, and stable airflow, Mauna Kea's summit is one of the best sites in the world for astronomical observation. Yes, I would say they changed my life. I search the universe for life. It's my hope one day I will see the Blue Men again. Before leaving the Blue Men, I asked them if I would see them again and they told me: 'Watch the skies. We are always there, watching and observing.' So that's what I do. I watch the skies."

Although I return to Hawaii almost every year, I have not seen Mele again. I think of him occasionally when I watch the night skies over my home in Montana. Like him, I hope someday to see the Blue Men.

8. SHERMAN'S STORY: SAVED FROM THE REPTILIANS BY THE BLUE MEN

I arrived in Binger, Oklahoma, on a cold, blustery day in January. I had come seeking a veteran with a story about reptilian creatures he encountered during his tour of duty in Vietnam. I drove slowly down the main street, looking for the Caddo Indian Government Offices. While his name was familiar to the young receptionist, she had no knowledge of him. Finally, she directed me to a family, who might help in my search. I discovered that Sherman, the individual I was trying to locate, was not a resident of Binger but was living in an elder center specializing in working with veterans suffering from terminal diseases in a city some eighty miles away. After numerous dead ends, I finally located Sherman. When I introduced myself and told him I met a marine in Hawaii who gave me his name, a broad smile crossed his face as he recognized the name of his old friend, Chester.

"You will have to sit close to me," Sherman said, "or your tape recorder might not pick up my voice. I'm a victim of 'Nam in more ways than one. Not only was I nearly blinded, but I suffer from COPD."

While he settled himself in a leather recliner near the end table, I set up my tape recorder. Sherman was a small man. He stood no more than five-feet-two-inches tall and probably weighed no more than a hundred pounds. His wiry black hair, peppered with gray, reminded me of several elders I saw in the reception area of the Caddo Government Hall. He wore thick-rimmed glasses, which he admitted did not help much, so he had long ago given up reading, which was his favorite form of entertainment.

"I spend my days listening to the radio and books on tape. After the war, I suffered from PTSD. Because of this, I never married. I'm the last of a long line of family warriors. It's for the best. If I'd lived a normal life, married, and had children, I'd probably have had a son or grandson in Iraq and Afghanistan. Too many senseless wars, but that's not why you're here. You don't want to hear the life story of an old dying Indian man."

"I'd love to hear your life story," I said, "and I've got all the time in the world. I'm at your disposal."

Sherman smiled.

"It's a good thing I never met you in my younger days. I might have broke my vow of bachelorhood," he said, chuckling loudly. "But first things first, I have never told anyone this story, except for Chester. Perhaps it's time the world knows about the reptile men." I watched as he closed his eyes, leaned back in his recliner and spoke in almost a stage whisper.

"I joined the Marine Corps as soon as I was eighteen," Sherman began. "I didn't wait for the draft. Being small, I guess I wanted to prove something to myself and maybe the world, that a small man could join the Marines. I graduated from Paris Island and was sent to 'Nam immediately. When I arrived in-country, I had no idea what was in store for me, but I found out the second day I was there." He paused, pushed the lever on his recliner and came to a sitting position with a thud. He reached for a glass of water, took two sips, adjusted his breathing canula, and then continued.

"I was in-country no more than forty-eight hours when word came to our unit that a tunnel had been located. If you don't know about the tunnels, it is something out of another world. The VC dug tens of thousands of miles of tunnels underneath the Cu Chi district northwest of Saigon. They used them to house troops, transport supplies, mount surprise attacks, and set booby traps. Whenever one was discovered, 'tunnel rats' would go into the tunnels to sabotage their underground network, kill any VC inside, set up explosives, and blow up the tunnels. A network of small access holes about two feet wide and three feet deep accessed their tunnel system."

"Were you a tunnel rat?" I asked.

He nodded.

"As I said, on the second day I was there, I was taken to a place where South Vietnamese soldiers, who were on our side, trained Americans to navigate the tunnels. There were also Aussies and Kiwis in training. We were chosen, along with others, because of our size, which was similar to the stature of the Viet Cong, to become a part of that program. Following the training, it was a matter of days before I was crawling on my hands and knees through these tunnels. I was given a flashlight, a pistol, and a knife. They were my only protection."

"Did you ever think of refusing to become a tunnel rat?"

"Refusing such a duty meant immediate court martial, and I did not want to spend the war in lock-up, but that idea never occurred to me. I loved the exhilaration of crawling through the tunnels and sabotaging the VC. I figured when I destroyed a tunnel, I saved dozens of American lives."

"What kind of men became tunnel rats?" I asked.

"We were an arrogant bunch. We stayed to ourselves to maintain our sanity. We were each other's support. We never took drugs and bragged about doing a job that no sane man would do. We frequently questioned the brass. We hated the second lieutenants. The college boys who knew nothing about war except what they had learned from textbooks."

"How did they feel about you?" I asked.

"I think they were afraid of us. Like I said, any man who would go into those tunnels had to be half-crazy. I think they saw us as a threat. Fragging was more common than most people know. Do you know about fragging?"

"I think so. Wasn't fragging the deliberate killing of a fellow soldier?"

"Usually it was an NCO or a second lieutenant. As the war dragged on and it was common knowledge that we were losing, fragging became more frequent, and the officers more afraid."

Sherman closed his eyes again, pulled the lever on the side

of his recliner, and remained silent as if revisiting those years in Vietnam. "We did some bad things in 'Nam," he said. I noted the regret in his voice.

"Was it in one of the tunnels where you encountered the reptilians?" I asked. Sherman nodded and continued his story.

"I had just returned from R&R in Hawaii. After thirteen months in Vietnam, we were allowed to go on leave for seven days. I chose Hawaii, even though it was generally the destination of married soldiers, because I was not interested in Southeast Asian prostitutes. I loved Hawaii. I should have moved there when some of my friends took up residence there. Chester invited me, but I stayed in the Oklahoma hills where I was born. If I had it to do over, I would be a Hawaiian. Don't you think I could pass for a Native?" he asked, smiling.

"I think that you would easily pass for a Native Hawaiian," I said.

He sat up again and looked out the sliding glass doors.

"During my first thirteen months in 'Nam I probably set charges and searched more than ten dozen tunnel openings. I never once encountered a VC, unlike some of my buddies. Several met their death in those tunnels." He paused as though remembering those who had lost their lives. "The day after I returned from R&R, a tunnel entrance was found. Reportedly, the brass believed that this was a key tunnel that linked villages and VC support bases all the way to the Cambodian border. Reportedly, there had been a number of strange activities going on in the area, and the brass thought it was a key entry point to the tunnel network."

"Did you go in alone?"

"Two of us were sent in. Sheldon, an Aussie, and me. It was a multi-level tunnel, going four stories down. Once I skirted through the entryway on my stomach, I was in a small room high enough for me to stand. I signaled Sheldon who joined me in a few minutes. The room was furnished with a table that contained a variety of bomb-making materials and several containers filled with rounds of rifle shells. We also found some military rations and bags of rice stashed next to the walls. We set a charge and continued along the tunnel. We traveled through several underground sleeping chambers. There were hammocks, made from US parachute nylon strung between bamboo poles. After that we thought we had reached a dead end. We could not find any more trap doors. The walls seemed solid rock or packed clay dirt. We were getting ready to return topside, when Sheldon leaned against a wall and fell through it. There we found a long narrow passageway. We crawled through a smooth tube-like tunnel. It was maybe twenty feet long."

"How far were you down at this point?" I asked.

"Maybe twenty feet underground. It was the fourth level as I recall."

"And at this point, you had not encountered any Viet Cong, correct?"

"Correct. When I exited the narrow tunnel, I found myself in a well-lit room, larger than any I had encountered. I waited for Sheldon, who joined me within seconds. The sight, too, astounded him. Neither of us could locate the source of the light, but the room was as bright as daylight. The walls around the room were like smooth, polished stone. Off to the left of us, a stone door stood. It was larger than any normal door, which was confusing to us since the VC were small men. As we approached the door, looking for another tunnel, we heard noises coming from the behind the door. We readied our weapons, planning to kill anything that came inside. That's when we saw the reptile men."

"Did you fire at them?" I asked.

"I never got off a shot. They were frightening figures, especially for an Indian boy from Oklahoma. Sheldon whispered that we had to get out of this place, but it was too late. Just as we saw them, they saw us. They were not like humans. I would say they stood about eight feet tall and were a brownish-green color. They moved like lightening. Sheldon fired but the bullet hit the ceiling. Their bright yellow eyes with black cat like pupils were evil. As they attacked us, I noticed only three fingers on their hands that were more like claws than human hands. Their noses were slits and their faces were flat. They actually looked like lizards. Although they stood upright on huge, bulbous legs, they had a huge tail which allowed them to move swiftly across the floor. They had a strange collar around their necks that appeared as a part of their body. It reminded me of a turtle shell where the head could be retracted in time of sleep or threat."

"How did they react when they saw you?" I asked.

"They hissed and gurgled among themselves. They pounced on us, lifted us off the ground, and threw us against the wall. As they continued to hiss, they showered us with some kind of substance they ejected from their mouths. While I was lying on the floor, I saw them walk through another stone door and disappear. Sheldon and I picked up our rifles. Both of us were dizzy and had trouble seeing, but we made our way to the stone door where we saw the reptile men disappear before our very eyes. After that, I lost consciousness. I'm not sure how long I lay there, but when I woke, I was outside the tunnel. At first, I didn't know how I got there, but hovering over me was a glowing blue giant who assured me that he meant me no harm."

Sherman sat up abruptly and launched into an endless coughing session. Each time he stopped, the coughing began again. I offered him water, but he pushed it away. After several minutes, he began again. "After we climbed to safety, we detonated our handiwork and that was the end of the reptile men's hidden underground tunnel. But to this day, I suffer. That's why my eyesight is so poor. In fact, it turned out to be my last tunnel. Because of my eyesight, the Marines sent me to a hospital in Hawaii to recuperate, and several months later, I was put on disability. That's where I met Chester. I kept in touch with Sheldon for several years, and he became blind shortly after leaving the military. I was a little luckier. Despite my disability, I was able to work at labor jobs. Nothing that required driving or reading and writing, but I earned a good pension despite my eyesight."

"What do you think the substance was?"

"I think it was like a snake venom. I think it was meant to kill us, in fact, but our protective gear and helmets saved us. When they hissed at us, a long-forked tongue came out of the slit in their tongue and showered us with their venom. As I saw the protruding tongue, I pushed my face into the floor and covered my face. My hands still show the effects of the poison." He flipped the lever on his chair again and came to a sitting position. He reached his hands across the end table between us. I saw the deep scars on his hand. "That's what the alien venom did to me," he said. "I suppose they thought we would never recover and die in that tunnel."

"Did you tell your commanding officers about the event?"

"Are you kidding? We knew they wouldn't believe us. The medics thought we'd encountered a bio-hazardous material in the tunnel and ordered us into a hospital. I was in several hospitals. Sheldon and I spent six months, first in Germany and then Hawaii, before the military decided to send us home. I told Chester about the event. He's the only person who knew the truth, but now, you. I never thought much about flying saucers and all that stuff. I considered it nonsense. I lived in the real world. But the reptile men were as real as you and me. The Blue Men were as real as you and me. I can confirm there are beings in this universe which do not look like human beings, who are smarter than us, and can travel the universe. Some are good; some are evil. That should humble us humans, don't you think?"

I took Sherman to dinner that night. He told me a shortened version of his life history over a bottle of expensive red wine. As I listened to him, I was humbled to be in the presence of this wonderful man who had lived more lives than a cat but still maintained a love for life that allowed him to flirt outrageously with me. He made no excuses for his behavior, and I felt he needed none.

I have not seen Sherman since my visit with him. In February, I sent him a box of candy, the complete works of Tony Hillerman on tape and a birthday card. I got a note from one of the nurses saying Sherman enjoyed the box of candy and card. He was now on his second round of listening to the Hillerman books. She said he was still doing well and would have written, but his eyesight has grown worse. She said he wanted me to return for another visit and another bottle of wine. I planned to do that on my next trip to Oklahoma. Until that time, I signed up with one of the wine catalogue companies to send him a bottle of wine along with assorted chocolates and cheese every month over the next year. It's the least I can do for the last of a long line of Caddo warriors.

9. NANOSE'S STORY: THEY TOOK MY FRIENDS

Nanose contacted me after a former student announced that I was known as the UFO Lady at a local basketball Appreciation Night. He stopped me in the parking lot as I struggled to open the hatch to my Subaru. After assisting me, Nanose told me that he had an encounter and needed to tell someone. He invited me to have breakfast with him the next morning. When I agreed, a wide grin crossed his face and he shook my hand vigorously. Little did I know that his story was not the usual Star People encounter.

I watched the tall, broad-shouldered man in military fatigues walk slowly toward my table. He sat down, examined the salt and pepper shakers, tightened them, and looked at me and grinned. He was a handsome man in his mid-thirties. An eagle ring graced his right hand, and an eagle feather earring hung from his left ear, occasionally catching in his long, black hair, which fell loosely below his shoulders.

After we ordered a pot of coffee and donuts, Nanose leaned forward and spoke to me in quiet voice. "I saw the Blue Men from outer space in Iraq," he said. "In my wildest dreams I would never have believed that men who had blue skin and glowed like the moon even existed. But I'm here to tell you, there are Blue Men. They come from outer space. They are giants, but gentle, peaceful men."

"Can you take me back to when and where you encountered them?" I asked.

"I enlisted in the military in 2001 when I was twenty, mostly out of boredom. There were no jobs on the reservation and everyone just hung out, smoked grass, and drank. I got tired of that lifestyle after a couple of years. I wasn't smart enough to get a scholarship to go to college, so I decided to let Uncle Sam send me to school. This was before the 9/11 event, and I didn't expect to end up on a battlefield, but in 2004 I was sent to Iraq." He paused as the waitress appeared with a plate of assorted donuts. "I don't tell strangers I'm a veteran. I don't like to talk about it. Telling you about the Blue Men is my first exception."

"How long have you been out of the Army?" I asked.

"I was in Middle East two years and twenty-three days. I've been home now ten years and one day. The Army offered money to reenlist but there was no way I was taking a chance on going to war again. War is like hell must be." He paused, looked over the plate of donuts and chose a jelly-filled roll. "I count myself lucky to have survived. I managed to get out of it what I wanted, a college degree. But it's of little use. No jobs for a fitness trainer on the rez. I suppose I could teach P.E, but I don't think I would make a good teacher. Besides, it doesn't take much for me to be right back there in Iraq in my mind. I reckon it will always be with me."

"What happened to you in Iraq?" I asked.

"Many things, but what I'm going to tell you is not something you will hear on TV. Lost or missing soldiers were not reported. The government closely guarded the deaths of Americans in Iraq. But the reason I wanted to talk to you was to tell you what happened to me and my buddies in Iraq. You can believe it or not, because even now when I think about it, it seems unbelievable." He became silent, shook his head as in disbelief and ate the donut in three bites. "I'm not a man to waste my time or your time. I swear to you this story is true." He paused again, wiped his hands on a napkin, and took a drink of his coffee.

"I make no judgments about the stories I hear," I said. "I am here to listen and to record your story."

"Okay. That's what I wanted to hear. One evening, our advanced patrol unit came under mortar attack. Several of our team was wounded or dead. After falling back and darkness fell around us, our lieutenant called for volunteers to retrieve the bodies of our comrades. My buddy Rense and I set out. It took us maybe twenty minutes to locate the first body. There were four down. Rense and I started to place the lifeless bodies into bags, when all of a sudden, I saw a light come out of the hills. I motioned for Rense to look in the direction of the light, but when I looked at him, he seemed stunned or under some kind of a spell. I shook Rense, but he didn't respond. While I'm trying to figure out what's going on, my eyes kept moving toward a mesmerizing light—a beautiful blue light. I couldn't determine where it came from, but it held me transfixed. As it came toward me, I made out the form of two men, giant men that were blue. As they approached me, I pointed my rifle at them, but they told me they meant no harm. My rifle slipped to the ground automatically, like some force was telling me it was okay."

"Did they tell you what they wanted?" I asked.

"They told me that they could take my friends with them— my dead comrades—and they could live again on another world. I didn't know what to make of it. I called out to Rense, but he didn't respond. Then they told me that Rense would have no memory of the events that were taking place and that soon they would return for him."

"Where were they going to take them?"

"They said they would have a good life, but not one on this Earth. I was in a dilemma. I didn't know what to do. I knew their families back home would want to bury their dead, but at the same time, the offer of a renewed life was appealing and I told them to take them."

"Can you describe the Blue Men?" I asked.

"They had a human form, but they were blue. Their bodies, or maybe it was their suits, were a luminescent blue. A beautiful blue."

"Did you trust them?"

"It's funny. I trusted them completely, and yet I knew they were not of this Earth. I felt total peace and contentment in their presence."

"What happened next?"

"The next thing I knew, Rense and I were searching for the bodies. He had no memory of any of the events. We searched for another half hour or so and then returned to our unit. We reported that we couldn't find any bodies." He paused, finished off another donut and drank his coffee before continuing.

"How do you feel about what you did that night?" I asked.

"I made a decision. I felt a chance for another life was best for my buddies. Maybe I'm wrong, but when I meet St. Peter at those pearly gates, I'll tell him I did my best."

"What about Rense? Did he ever remember that night?"

"Rense was blown up on a patrol the next night. I was with him, but there was nothing I could do. His body came up missing. I believe the Blue Men found him and took him away, too. It's strange, you know. It was like the Blue Men knew his fate. They told me they would return for him soon, but at the time I thought nothing of it. I didn't realize they were foretelling his future. They knew he was going to die." He ate another donut and poured another cup of coffee from the carafe left by the waitress.

"Obviously, these events have had a profound impact on your life. How are you dealing with it?"

"I've often thought about contacting Rense's family and explaining that I believe their son is alive and living on another planet, and then I stop and think about how crazy that sounds. Then I think maybe knowing that their son was alive and on another planet would be worse than thinking he was dead. I'm satisfied that he has a good life; the Blue Men promised me that. My only regret is that I didn't go with them, too."

"Did they offer to take you?" I asked.

He nodded. I saw the tears welling up in his eyes and decided to change the subject.

"You said you graduated from college. Where are you working now?"

"I'm a firefighter. My degree didn't do me much good. No jobs on the reservation even for a college graduate. I also work a little construction when there are no fires. Anything to pay the bills.

I have a small cabin out in the country where my grandpa lives. When I'm not working, I watch TV and play computer games. I read a lot. I have a tomato garden that I tend. We don't have running water, so it's small. I'd like to have a big garden, but the lack of water makes it difficult. I like the quietness of the country. No cars, planes, or people; only Grandpa, and he's a quiet man, too. Sometimes we sit at night and watch the stars. I keep hoping that when the good Lord takes Grandpa, the Blue Men will come for me, too. Every night, I whisper a silent prayer for their return, but so far they have not appeared."

On my next visit to the reservation, I visited Nanose at his home in the country and met his grandfather, Abraham. He still keeps to himself and prefers not to talk about the war, but when there is just the two us, he speaks openly about the Blue Men. Although he has been invited many times to reservation celebrations for veterans, Nanose never attends. He is still waiting for the Blue Men and struggling to come to grips with the decision he made that night. He told me that his name, Nanose, meant cougar in English. He believes that his name foretold his ability to go to war and stealthily, like the cat of his nomenclature, make his way through the war-torn country and survive. As for me, I believe Nanose is a survivor, and his name gives him amazing spiritual powers; he just hasn't realized it yet.

10. MATOSKA'S STORY: I HOPE THEY RETURN FOR ME

Matoska was a twenty-four-year-old army vet who emailed me while in Afghanistan and told me that when he returned stateside, he would like to meet me. He said a most unusual event happen to him while on patrol one night, and it was a story that should be told. We agreed to meet at a pre-arranged site in Colorado, halfway between my home and his.

I met Matoska at a rest stop off the interstate. Dressed in camouflaged pants and an olive-green t-shirt, I recognized him immediately from his description. Standing well over six-feet tall, he would have stood out in almost any crowd. He walked me to a covered cement picnic table at the interstate rest stop. In the center of the table stood a cooler. "My grandma taught me that when you invite guests, you always bring food," he said as he offered me a submarine sandwich. "I have an assortment of drinks," he continued.

"Water is fine," I said as I unwrapped my sandwich. I kept an eye on the young man who told me he was Indian but could have been at home among many ethnic groups.

"I guess you're wondering who I am. For the record, my mama was Lakota and Southern Cheyenne, and my dad was white man from Finland. That's the reason for my name, Matoska. It means white bear. I was an only child. My mom raised me after my dad decided he missed Finland. She refused to go with him, and we never heard from him again."

"It's his loss," I replied as I noted the sadness in his voice.

Matoska sighed and took a bite of his sandwich. He watched

an 18-wheeler pull into the rest stop, and before I could make an attempt at reassuring the nervous former marine who sat across from me, he blurted out, "Have you ever heard of the Blue Men?"

I nodded. His shoulders relaxed as though a load had been lifted from his shoulders. He jumped up, clasped both of my hands and looked upward and mumbled words often associated with praising God. "Yes, yes, yes!" he exclaimed. "I knew it all along. Others have seen the Blue Men, too!"

I watched a broad smile cross his face as he seated himself across the table from me again. He reached out, clasped my hands, planted a kiss on them, and then whispered, "Thank you."

"Can you tell me about your encounter?" I asked.

He nodded and caught his breath. "I saw the Blue Men in Afghanistan," he said. "The brightest blue, translucent color you can imagine. I've never told anyone this story but, thank God, I heard one of your interviews on YouTube about Star People. I knew I had to contact you. Thank you for meeting me. I know that meeting a stranger at a rest stop is unusual, but I needed privacy and you know what it's like in an Indian home—too many relatives." He paused and laughed.

"I'm happy to meet you."

He nodded and took a bite of his sandwich. Then he opened a bag of potato chips and offered me one before continuing.

"I deployed to Kandahar in January 2010. I was a Communications Operator. I operated and maintained communications equipment from combat radios to satellite phones. We were short-handed in that area of expertise. I shared that responsibility with one other operator, so we had twelve hours on and twelve hours off. On my down time, I often went on patrol into the city. Part of it was out of boredom, and part of it was because I grew fond of the children in the city. Growing up I always thought Indians were poor, but there's nothing like the poverty and suffering of the Afghani children." He paused and took a sip of his Pepsi before continuing. "One night as I was monitoring the combat radios, I got an urgent message for emergency medical evacuations. Our troops were wounded by a roadside bomb and others were under heavy fire. Under those conditions, Med Air Evac Teams couldn't deploy immediately to pick up the wounded."

"Were American soldiers killed that night?" I asked.

He nodded. "But you won't hear about it on *CNN*. So many things are covered up about what is going on over there." He took another bite of his sandwich and placed it on the wrapper. "The next day, we were sent out to recover the bodies. I volunteered to go; these men were my brothers."

"What did you discover?"

"We rescued only one soldier, Dustin, who had made it through the night."

"Were there casualties?"

"The other seven were missing. We found some signs of their existence, a rifle, a St. Christopher medal, but no bodies."

"What happened to them?"

"Dustin said he didn't know, but late the next night, he told me an amazing story. He claimed that the Star Men came for them."

"The Star Men?"

"According to him, he took refuge in a building and decided to wait out the night. The others were outside, and even though he called for them throughout the night, no one came. About an hour after radio silence, he told me he saw a bright light. All gunshots were silenced and a beam came down, and he watched them recover the bodies one by one and lift them into a tubular craft that rested above the scene."

"Did he remember any other details?" I asked.

"He said that as the event was happening, he couldn't take his eyes off it. He yelled at his buddies, but none of them responded."

"Did he ever see the Star Men?" I asked.

"He said that after the bodies were recovered, the Star Men came to him."

"Did he tell you what they looked like?"

"He said they were tall, blue men, maybe as tall as eight feet. Very muscular and strong. They told him they were going to take his friends. They also told Dustin his friends would be fine and that he would survive his tour of duty and return home to his wife and children."

"Was he interrogated by his commanding officer?" I asked.

"He never told the brass what happened. He said he couldn't remember."

"Did his superiors believe him?"

"They found no reason not to. Everything was kept hush-hush. There was no way to explain the disappearance of seven soldiers and the press would have a field day. It was covered up."

"What about their families?"

"The most interesting thing about the whole event was that none of the missing soldiers had listed a next of kin. So it was easy to keep it out of the press. Americans never knew what happened that night, only Dustin who was determined to maintain silence."

"Why do you think he kept silent?" I asked.

"Do you think anyone would have believed him?"

"Probably not."

"Dustin wanted to make a career out of the military. He was probably afraid to tell them what he saw for fear he would be discharged for psychological reasons."

"Did you believe his story?"

"At the time, I wasn't sure what to believe. I knew the bodies were never recovered. It may not have made *CNN*, but that doesn't mean it didn't happen. I knew those guys. They were my friends, as close as any brother, and they were gone."

"So you never revealed your friend's story until now?"

"Well, that isn't the end of the story. Two days later, I went with Dustin on patrol. As we toured the streets that day, the heat was unbearable. We went into a deserted building to escape the heat. It was so hot in Afghanistan that you could fry an egg on a rock in the sun. It was miserable, and we were wearing heavy equipment, protective vests, and backpacks filled with survival equipment and tools. We just wanted a reprieve from the sun and to drink some water." He paused and finished off his sandwich and a can of Pepsi.

"Did something happen inside the building?"

"Something amazing happened." He paused again and opened another can of Pepsi. "After searching the building, we positioned ourselves against a wall and watched the doorway. I remember relaxing a little and enjoying the coolness of the building, and that's when it happened. Out of nowhere, the Blue Men materialized before us. They told us that our friends were fine, and they were able to save our fallen comrades. All seven were alive and well."

"Alive and well, but I thought they were dead. Isn't that what you told me?" I asked.

"They said they took them away to live in another world free of war. Their past memories were gone and new memories in their place so they would no longer remember the war or their life on Earth."

"How did you react to that?"

"At first, I felt angry. I thought they had no right to play God. Just as I was about to tell them this, I realized I was in the presence of powerful beings that were good and humane. They were the best part of what humans could be. Then they disappeared just as they appeared, but before going they told Dustin that they would put his mind at ease."

"What did your friend say about their appearance?"

"That's the strange thing about it. When I mentioned the Blue Men, he looked at me like I was crazy and said he didn't know anything about Blue Men and wanted to know if I had been sipping the home brew. It soon became obvious to me that he had no memory of the events. I never spoke to him about it again. I don't know why I remembered. But I swear to you on the Bible, which I believe is Holy, this happened just as I told you."

He paused and picked up our sandwich papers and walked to the garbage can. "I don't think they were gods, but they were godly men, who monitor our wars and sometimes they choose humans to save."

"What about the young men who were taken? Did you do any investigation about what they may have had in common?"

"It's funny you should mention that. I did do that. One night when everyone was resting, I looked at the files. They were all between the ages of twenty and twenty-four. There were two Mexicans who joined the army to get citizenship. There were two white guys from Alabama. There was one black soldier from Mississippi. There were two Indians. They listed no tribal affiliation, only Native American. Both listed their residence as Oklahoma. And as I mentioned before, they listed no relatives. They were alone in the world. Perhaps the Blue Men chose them for that reason. When I thought about it, I felt better. At least no one was at home mourning them. I think Dustin escaped because he was married with a wife and children."

"Why didn't they take you?" I asked.

"When they appeared before Dustin and me, I think they came to help him forget. And me, I was a non-combatant. I was a radioman who just happened to go on patrol with Dustin. If they had given me the option to go, I might have considered it, although I do love my mom. I love her a lot. Besides she was listed as my next of kin."

"Do you think they knew that?"

"They chose carefully who they took. Men with no ties to Earth."

"So you see the Blue Men as peaceful and loving. Is that correct?"

"I see the Blue Men as men from the stars who love peace and gave my friends another chance. They were in a war not of their making. They were dead according to all reports."

"Would you ever go with them?

"Someday when my mom passes, I hope they will return for me. I would like to live in their world."

I never saw Matoska again. I do get an occasional email from him, but he never mentions the Blue Men. He always signs his emails with a quote: "Still watching the Sky.... White Bear." I think of Matoska often. He was not the first veteran who has told me about an encounter with the Blue Men. I cannot help but wonder, how many other veterans have had the same experience but keep silent.

11. WINTER'S STORY: GLOWING BLUE MEN TOUCHED MY BRAIN

Winter was celebrating his graduation from high school at a friend's party when his dreams of the future were destroyed by a car accident fueled by alcohol. Left paralyzed from the waist down, a paralyzed right arm, and blind in one eye, his dream of studying medicine vanished that night. After two years of surgery and rehabilitation, he suffered from extreme depression and had attempted suicide twice. I had watched Winter and his sister grow up. His parents, who were both educators, often invited me to dinner when I visited the reservation. It was on such a night, when his parents were attending a tribal council meeting, that I sat with Winter and he told me about his life-saving ordeal and the Star People.

Winter greeted me when I entered his home. He moved his wheelchair in a circular rotation and invited me into the living room. His mother and father were nowhere to be seen. "The folks are upstairs getting ready for the meeting. Big night tonight. They're voting on a resolution to expand tribal membership. I made some popcorn and got a bottle of Diet Coke in your honor and a bucket of ice. So we're set," he said as he maneuvered his wheelchair across from a chair that faced the big picture window.

As I settled myself, his parents appeared, and after a short greeting and a hug, they left. I sat down in the chair again.

"I asked to talk with you privately," Winter said as I heard the front door close.

"Your parents told me you wanted to see me."

"I'm glad you're here. I trust you. I wanted to tell my story to someone I trust. I've not only known you forever, but I found your books on Amazon and read them on Kindle. There are a couple of stories of encounters in your book that are similar to mine, but not exactly."

"I like to tape my interviews and take notes."

Winter nodded and watched as I placed the tape recorder on the side table between us and took out my notebook.

"Have you spoken about your encounter with your parents?"

"God no. They have enough to deal with. Look at me. I not only destroyed my life that night, but I destroyed theirs. There are some things I keep to myself. But after reading your books, it got me to thinking. If my story can help someone else, I'm willing to share it."

"I'm glad to hear that. Where would you like to begin?" I asked.

"I guess the best place is the graduation party. I got wasted that night. In fact, I don't even remember getting in the car with Amelia. She was kinda my girlfriend but nothing serious. I had a singular goal and that was to be a doctor and return here, work at the hospital, get married, and raise a bunch of kids."

"I remember that was your goal when you were ten," I said. "What happened that night, or do you remember?"

"Actually, I don't remember much. Butch, my best friend, told me that two of the guys carried me to the car and Amelia got behind the wheel. She had been drinking too, but they thought she was okay to drive. As you know, the drive to our place is over a mountain road with a couple of hairpin curves, and she missed one and drove right over the embankment. The car tumbled end over end until it came to rest against a tree, no more than ten feet from the river."

"I've seen the site of the accident. The Great Spirit was looking out for you that night."

"I don't know about that, but one thing's for sure, someone was watching out for me," Winter said.

"Were you conscious when it happened?"

"Not at first. I remember the pain and waking up with blood dripping down my face. I couldn't move. I called for someone to help but got no answer."

"How do the Star Men fit into this equation?" I asked.

"I was trapped by the back seat, which had collapsed against the front passenger's seat. I called out to Amelia, but she was unresponsive. I learned later that she had died on impact. I feel bad about that. Amelia was my best friend and the smartest girl I'd ever met. It took a long time for me to accept her death. She wanted to go to nursing school. When we were little, we often said I'd be a doctor; she would be my nurse."

"So you regained consciousness after the accident. Is that correct?" I asked trying to get him to refocus. He looked at me. I saw the tears in his eyes.

"Yes, but immovable. I had no feeling in my legs and feet. I panicked and pounded on the door. I yelled until my voice rasped. No one came, so I gave up. I tasted the blood in my mouth and knew I was not likely to survive unless help came immediately. That's when it happened."

"Are you referring to the Star People?" I asked.

He nodded. "Suddenly a bright, iridescent, blue light descended upon the car, and I thought the police discovered the accident. That's when I saw a being engulfed in a strange, glowing blue light. I couldn't make out any features. I thought I must be dead and the ancestors had come for me to take me to spirit world."

"Can you describe anything about the entities you saw?"

He paused for a moment, poured the Coke into the glasses with his left hand and offered me the bowl of popcorn. For a moment we sat there in silence, while we both ate a handful of popcorn and drank our sodas. "It's not easy to describe them. The image is fuzzy in my mind. I know they had the form of humans, but there was a shimmering glow that distorted their image. It was hard to get a clear image."

"Did they speak to you?"

"Not at first. One of them pulled the back door off the sedan and threw it aside like it was a toy. The other one came in from behind me and tore the other door off and removed the back seat that was trapping me. The one behind me placed his hands on my head and the bleeding stopped. I felt a healing in my head. My head felt so hot that I thought it would explode. As he covered my head with his hands, he said I should not be afraid."

"Did you feel afraid?"

"Once he touched me, peace filled my body. I was no longer afraid. I knew I was going to survive."

"What did he do to your head?"

"They healed the opening in my head. When I got to the hospital, there was only a scar that the doctors could not explain." He leaned forward and parted his long black hair. I saw the white scar about a quarter of inch wide and three inches long. "They asked me about it, but I had no idea. But I knew it was the Star Men. They did something to my head. In fact, I think if they had not come to me, I would have died from loss of blood or been mentally incapacitated for the rest of my life. I think they saved my life and made it so I could continue to function mentally."

"If they have so much power, why didn't they heal your paralysis?" I asked.

"They removed me from the car and placed me against a tree. They told me that interference with another's destiny was not a standard practice for them, but they made an exception in my case."

"Did they tell you why?"

"They said that my destiny had already been decided. I didn't understand it. Days after the accident, I felt angry. These beings were powerful, and I believe they could have healed my physical condition and they chose not to do that."

"So have you accepted your paralysis?"

"It hasn't been easy. The first year I was angry; so angry that I lashed out against people who tried to help me. I said terrible things to them that I regret."

"I think that's normal. The important thing is not to beat yourself up about that," I said, trying to reassure him.

"I still have bouts of depression. I want to die sometimes. But there is one thing that keeps me from doing it."

"Do you mean related to the Star Men?"

"Yes. Something happened to me when they healed my head. I hope you won't think I'm crazy. You know I've always been a good student. I graduated valedictorian. But something happened that night that is difficult to explain."

"Please try," I said. He took a drink of his Coke and drew a long breath.

"I have increased mental ability. I can't explain it. In the hospital, I discovered I could read a book in a day. I asked my mom to bring me a dictionary, a big one. She brought a huge one from the school library—you know the kind that weighs a ton and generally sits on a table because it's too heavy to move."

I nodded.

"I read the entire thing. I began noticing other things. I had to tone down my vocabulary when I talked to my friends who visited me. My vocabulary was far beyond what I was capable of before the accident. I discovered I learned things more easily and was interested in almost every subject." He paused and ate another handful of popcorn. "I read all the classics literature, American and British. I committed poetry to memory. Math and science books were everyday reading for me."

"Do you believe the aliens did something that increased your intelligence?" I asked.

"I believe the aliens, when they repaired my head, did something to my brain. Yes. I believe they increased my intelligence."

"Have you ever considered going to the university?"

"I would have to have a caretaker. I can't go to the bathroom by myself," he said. I noticed the first sign of defeatism and reached for his hand. He offered a weak smile, and I saw the tears forming in his eyes.

"Winter, there are all kinds of help for disabled students including caretakers. Maybe you're not supposed to be a doctor. Maybe the Star Men knew that. You're definitely an intelligent young man. I know you wanted to be a surgeon, but perhaps you should go into medical research. Maybe you'll find a way to reverse paralysis for accident victims. The possibilities are limitless. Perhaps the Star People knew your destiny did not need physical mobility."

A smile crossed his face and he wiped a tear from his cheek. "I think it was more than that. I wanted to be a doctor so I would be rich. Helping people took the backseat. I used to envision myself with a beautiful wife and beautiful children living in a big house and taking fabulous vacations."

"And now?"

He shook his head. "Beautiful girls don't want anything to do with me. What woman wants to be with a cripple?"

"You're not a cripple in your mind. Some women love men for their intellect. While it's true, you would need both hands and probably use of your legs to be a surgeon, there are other ways to make contributions in the medical field. Perhaps the Star People knew that and only improved your mental abilities."

"Do you think that's the reason they left me like this?" he asked.

"Who knows? I'm only speculating. But I think it's time you started counting your blessings and do something with your life."

"Is this what they call 'tough love'?" he asked smiling at me.

"Could be," I responded reaching for his hand. "I've heard of some amazing miracles involving Star People's intervention. Maybe they knew that in your case, being handicapped was a blessing. It would give you the right path to achieve your intended goals, even if you didn't know what they were. I hope you will take this opportunity that was given to you and imagine a different future for yourself."

"Maybe you're right." He smiled and reached for my hand again. "Did anyone ever tell you that you are one smart lady?" he asked. Before I could respond, he added, "I'm so glad you've been a part of my life and that you're friends with Mom and Dad. I've always thought of you as my second Mom. Someday I might be able to show you how much you mean to me."

"Find a cure for old age, and I will be thankful forever," I said smiling.

"Done," he said twirling in his wheelchair.

We spent the rest of the evening finishing off the bowl of popcorn and drinking the quart of Diet Coke, reliving the past and discussing possible options for his future.

Winter and I stay in contact on a regular basis. Every time I see him, I'm reminded that the Blue Men can and do perform miracles. Shortly after my visit, Winter enrolled at the tribal college and completed the core classes in six months instead of the two years expected of students. He transferred to the state university and enrolled in a pre-med program. Despite his disabilities, he is no longer the handicapped boy who once told me how his dreams were lost that fateful night. Instead he is a vibrant, intelligent young man who astounds his peers and his professors with his analytical skills and vast store of knowledge about pharmaceuticals and diseases. He has currently branched out into the study of robotics and their use in medical science. I expect great things of him in the future and expect he will make a difference in the world. I believe the Star People knew it, too.

12. MADISON'S STORY: A BLUE BALL OF LIGHT

Madison was an FBI agent on a southwestern reservation and a member of a California tribe. She had requested the post on this particular reservation because of the drug trafficking problem. Her brother had died of a drug overdose, leaving Madison with no relatives except a distant cousin who lived in Seattle. She vowed to bring down the members of various Mexican cartels operating on reservations. It was the night of one of her stakeouts that she had an encounter; an event that has made her re-evaluate her career decision.

I met Madison during a school lockdown. A student brought a weapon to school and was caught showing it to his friends, when the principal ordered the campus closed. At the time, I was a visiting consultant and was due to be in another school when the event occurred. The tribal police were the first to show up, followed by the Bureau of Indian Affairs (BIA) police. A local representative of Homeland Security arrived and barked orders to all of us who only wanted to flee the makeshift prison. When Madison, the FBI agent arrived, I approached her and asked her permission to leave the school premises. Even though she sympathized with my situation, there was little she could do. Realizing that I might be stuck there for countless hours, I found a place at the top bleacher in the gymnasium, pulled out my tape recorder and earphones, and began listening to an interview I had conducted the previous night. A police dog arrived and began searching row by row. Madison was wandering up and down the bleachers. When she saw me, she came over and sat down.

"Let's see, you look like an Aerosmith fan," she said.

I pushed the stop button on the tape recorder and took out my earphones.

"You're right. I'm a fan, but I wasn't listening to music, just reviewing an interview from last night."

She held out her hand and after brief introductions, she smiled and commented, "Now I remember where I heard your name. You're the UFO lady." I nodded. "I heard you were on the reservation and hoped I would meet you. I've been interested in your work and I've read your books, but I never expected to meet you."

"Thank you. I'm always happy to meet one of my readers."

"How many people have you interviewed on this reservation?" she asked.

"Twenty-three total," I replied.

"Can you tell me if the stories relate to encounters with aliens?"

"The people around here call them Star People, and, yes, I have interviewed individuals who have had direct encounters."

"How do you locate individuals who have had encounters?" she asked.

"I find them through acquaintances and relatives who refer them to me; other times the individuals seek me out, and on several occasions, I think it's fate. Frequently, I find myself in the right place at the right time and it's as if the story just comes to me. It's destiny. I can't explain it. I meet strangers who suddenly tell me they have a story of an encounter. It's like someone is intervening so I can tell their story."

"Do you believe in destiny?" she asked.

I nodded.

"I do too. Perhaps it was fated for the school to be lock downed because that would bring me here as part of the response team. And perhaps it was just fate that you happened to be caught in the lockdown. Fate or destiny?"

"I'm not sure I'm following you," I replied.

"I have a story, too," she explained. "I had an encounter that has made me question everything I've been taught. But I can't tell you now. I have to join the others. I don't think there is anything beyond the young man showing off to his classmates, but we have to be sure." She reached in her pocket and pulled out a business card. "If you're free tonight, let's get together over drinks. Call me later. My cell number is listed there."

Two hours later, the principal came over the intercom and announced that the lockdown was lifted and that guests were free to leave.

Madison and I got together about 8 p.m. that night at her home in the government housing section of the reservation. "Part of the perks of the job is housing," she said as we walked into her living room. "The house is far too big for me, so if you ever need a place to crash, feel free to give me a call. Have a seat and I will be back in a minute." I sat down in a large easy chair just as she returned from the kitchen with two huge glasses of strawberry daiquiris. "One virgin as requested and one with alcohol for me," she said as she set them on the coffee table. "You know, I'm breaking the law right now. This is a dry reservation and alcohol is forbidden. Of course, nine out of ten houses have alcohol of some kind, but that doesn't mean there isn't a law forbidding it. But there are times I enjoy being naughty," she said chuckling.

"You said you have a story to tell. I hope you don't mind if I tape it."

"Not at all. It was after my encounter that I began searching for books on the subject. Until then, I thought such stories were to attract attention. That's when I came across your books. I know you keep everything anonymous. I applaud your approach to your interviews. Many researchers don't understand why Indians don't talk to them. But you honor them with the way to treat them. They can be free and honest with you and they know you will not condemn them."

"That's important to me," I said.

"Well, let's get down to business. I will tell you my story."

I pushed the record button on the tape recorder and she began. "One of the worst things about my job is the waiting. I spend countless hours on stakeouts, and the waiting is boring and more often than not fruitless. One night a few months ago, I was on a stakeout of an alleged drug dealer. I suspected he was an illegal who was shacking up with a reservation girl and had ties to a Mexican cartel. I'm not sure how he came to be on the reservation, but it was not long before he found a woman, and with his green card, he was free to move back and forth across the border. That's a common practice among the drug runners. They can be found all over the west. Their method of operation often involves finding a local woman which gives them freedom of movement around the reservation and with a green card they freely move across the border."

"Do you carry out the stakeouts alone?"

"I'm the only FBI agent on the reservation. I keep the BIA police, who are also federal, advised of my operations when I go on a stakeout, but they don't assign anyone to work with me."

"How did you encounter the alien?" I asked.

"On this particular night, I had been on stakeout for seven hours. By 4 a.m., I was getting sleepy and decided to return home. There were two small hills along the highway with a one-lane bridge over the river. I crossed the first hill with no incident, but just as I approached a curve in the road, I noticed a brilliant blue ball hovering along the side of the road. I slowed. Frankly, I was mesmerized by the light. I wasn't sure what I saw, and just as I slowed, I saw a brilliant blue ball dart into the underbrush along the side of the road. I immediately stopped and shined a spotlight in the direction. I got out of my car, drew my weapon, and walked toward the edge of the road."

"Did you call in your position to the police?"

"No. It happened too fast. I kept walking up and down the edge of the highway until I came to the bridge. After the bridge there is a warning that alerts drivers about the next hill. There are barriers on each side of the bridge and steel posts to prevent cars from going into the river. As I shined my flashlight into the darkness beyond the bridge, I saw two men standing on the other side of the posts. When I ordered them to raise their hands and come toward me, a shot rang out missing me by inches."

"I thought you saw a blue, glowing ball. Were there men, too?" I asked.

"As I found out later, I had come across some drug peddlers, and at the moment they were shooting at me."

"Weren't you afraid?"

"I'm trained to take care of myself. I wasn't afraid at the time, but my bravery was short-lived. Suddenly I was aware of the glowing blue ball circling me. Just as I started to turn around, the ball of light engulfed me, and even though I could hear gunshots, they seem to ricochet off the blue ball. At that point, I struggled to escape the light and ran for my vehicle, but suddenly an entity grabbed me and the next thing I knew, my feet were off the ground and I was being escorted through the woods. I felt a sense of peace come over me and I did not resist."

"Did you ever see the entities that kidnapped you?" I asked.

"Only glimpses. They appeared human, but they were engulfed in this blue, shimmering light. They communicated in my head and told me not to fear. The next thing I remember is returning to the edge of the road. Suddenly the two drug traffickers walked up the bank with their hands raised. They asked me to arrest them. They had been so frightened by the blue light that they feared for their life. I called for backup from the tribal police. After an hour of searching, we recovered their stash of drugs."

"Did you have any idea who kidnapped you?" I asked.

"No. I saw no one. I only saw the blue glow."

"Where did they take you?" I asked.

"They carried me about a mile through the forest. As a person trained to observe, I tried to remember every single detail about my surroundings. I heard the river and saw a relay tower in the distance. At that point, I think I passed out." She paused and lit a cigarette. She took two puffs and stubbed it out in the ashtray. She paced nervously around the couch.

"That's my story. Have you heard anything similar?" she asked.

"I've heard of the balls of light and the Blue Men." I saw her relax as she took a long breath and exhaled. "The experience has changed my life forever. I know that life exists away from Earth. It might be different, but it exists."

Madison left the FBI two months after our meeting. She returned to the university and received a PhD in archaeology a few years later. The last I heard, she was somewhere in the jungles of Guatemala. She was part of a team excavating an ancient city in the rainforest.

13. RAYEN'S STORY: THE BLUE MEN AND A SPEEDING TRAIN

Rayen was a thirty-three-year-old mother of five-year-old twin girls and a seven-year-old son. She was a full-time homemaker. Her husband, Russell, was head of the sanitation department on the reservation. The two married shortly after high school, graduated from college, and delayed having children until they could make a down payment on their home and Rayen could quit her job. Rayen called me one night as I was just settling into bed of another shabby reservation motel room. She told me she had heard the rumors that I collected stories about UFO encounters and wondered if she could tell me her story. When I told her my schedule, she asked if it would be possible if she could visit with me in ten minutes. I agreed since I was never one to discourage someone with a story to tell.

I no sooner put on a robe when I heard a knock on the door of my motel room. Unlike most reservation women, she wore her hair in a short, stylish cut. It was obvious that she had not dressed for an evening out; the hole in her baggy sweat pants revealed she had probably planned to spend the evening at home relaxing with her family.

"I really, really appreciate that you are willing to see me. I know it is an imposition. I see you were ready for bed."

"I was about to read. You are not an imposition. I'm happy to meet with you."

"You're very kind. There aren't too many people who would get out of bed to listen to a story, but I'm hoping you can help me." I walked to the kitchenette in my room, opened the refrigerator, got out two bottles of water, and offered her one.

"I hope you don't mind if I tape your story."

She shook her head. "I don't mind, but no names please. I don't want anyone to know who I am."

"You have my word," I said.

"Where do you want me to start?" she asked.

"At the beginning is always a good place," I replied.

She nodded. I watched as she took off her shoes, pulled her legs and feet onto the couch, and rested her chin on her knees.

"I never much thought about UFOs. You'd have to live under a rock if you didn't know that people are abducted and UFO sightings are quite common, but I always paid little attention. I guess I really didn't believe the stories were true, except maybe the photos of the UFOs I'd seen on the History Channel or the internet. They looked real. But about a year ago, I became a believer."

"Can you tell me how that came about?"

"My encounter happened in the fall of last year. I went to the city to shop for school clothes and supplies for my kids. My mother-in-law told me she would babysit, so I left the kids home. Russell, my husband, was working that day so I went alone. I had a great day shopping. I met a college friend for lunch and finished my shopping by six and headed home. I had a two-hour drive ahead of me. I expected to arrive home by 8 p.m. Russell promised to feed the kids and put them to bed."

"Did you have your encounter on your drive home?"

She nodded, opened the bottle of water, and sipped it from the top. "It was on an isolated section of the road near the railroad crossing in Burgess. Have you ever traveled that road?"

"Many times."

"Well, then you know how quiet and remote that place is. The whole town is no more than a city block. It was particularly dark when I came through town. Generally, I see lights in windows and a lighted beer sign at the bar, something to show there was life. On this night, it was very dark. No lights, no people, not even a light in a house. It gave me an eerie feeling. I remember the hair standing up on my arms like static electricity. I slowed at the railroad crossing, looked both ways to make sure there was no train, and pulled onto the tracks. Suddenly I heard a thunderous sound and my Suburban began rocking. I looked up and a train was speeding down the rails with no lights. It was headed directly for me. There was no warning that a train was approaching the crossing. No barriers across the road. I stomped on the accelerator. There was no way I was going to make it. Then out of nowhere, I felt my car levitating."

"Levitating?"

"You know. Lifting off the ground. I opened the car door but there was nothing below me but darkness, but I swear, my car was moving upward and there was no place for me to go."

"Were there any unusual smells or sounds that you remember?"

"Nothing. After that I must have passed out. I woke in an unfamiliar place. There was nothing like it I had ever seen in my life."

"What do you mean an unfamiliar place?" I asked.

"Well, it wasn't long until I discovered I was on a spaceship. I found myself in a hot, humid, barely lit room. It was moist and smelled like rotting trees. My car was missing and I kept thinking that I still had two years to pay for it. I worried about how I would get home. It wasn't long until these strange entities—five of them—entered the room."

"Can you describe them?"

"They were blue. I know that sounds incredible, but they were huge beings, human-like in appearance but glowing, luminescent blue."

"Do you recall whether they communicated with you?"

"They spoke to me in English in my head. I heard voices in my brain."

"Did they tell you why you were on the spaceship?"

"Only that they had been observing the Earth, and they watched as I approached the crossing. They realized the train was going to collide with my vehicle and they decided to save me."

"Did they give you a reason?"

"No, and I was too hysterical to ask. I just wanted to be home. I knew they had saved me, but I just wanted to get away from them."

"Did anything else happen to you while you were on the craft?"

"I'm not sure. I tried to stay awake, but I couldn't. The next thing I remember, I was sitting in my car on the other side of the crossing and my car was running."

"When you got home, were you aware of what had happened to you?"

"It was almost midnight when I pulled into the garage. Russell opened the kitchen door and yelled at me, demanding to know where I had been. I told him the car quit working, and I was stranded on the side of the road until someone came along and restarted my battery. I was almost four hours late."

"So you lied. Why?" I asked.

"Because at the time, I thought it was more believable than what really happened." She got up from the couch and paced the floor. "I know I should have told the truth, but I can't bring myself to do it. Can you tell me, have you heard of blue space men? I can't get them out of my mind."

"I've heard of the blue men many times. I assure you it is more common than you might imagine."

She grabbed my hands and held on tight for a long time. "Thank you. That's all I wanted to know, and thanks for talking to me. I needed to know I was not alone and that there were others who had similar experiences. It means a lot to me."

Shortly thereafter, she excused herself and left. I stood in the doorway of my motel room and wondered if she would ever tell her husband the truth.

I've seen Rayen a few times since I first met her. She always greets me with a smile. While she has never told her husband the truth, she said they never speak of that night. Knowing that others have seen the Blue Men has helped her with her nightmares. So far, she has not seen them again.

14. SYLVIA'S STORY: A BLUE STAR MAN SAVED ME

When I first met Sylvia, she was leaving an Alcoholics Anonymous meeting at the Tribal Community Center. When she saw me, she approached and said she recognized me from the cover of my book, Encounters with Star People. She went on to tell me that she had read and reread the book at least a dozen times and wanted me to know that she knew the stories were true because she had also experienced an encounter. When I asked her if she would like to tell her story, she nodded and asked me to call her when I had time to talk with her. We met the next evening at an off-reservation McDonald's.

Sylvia, who was named for her great grandmother, Sylvia Red Feather, was a twenty-year-old tribal college freshman. She admitted to being a former drug addict and an alcoholic. She had been sober for twenty-two months at the time of our meeting. A petite young woman with troubled eyes, she spoke openly and without hesitation as we sat at a rear table in the back of the McDonald's dining area.

"I brought a lot of shame on my family," she began, pausing momentarily as she attacked the Big Mac on her tray. "It's the same old story. Nothing to do on the reservation. I was a bored teenager. I hated school and chose the wrong crowd. Every time I got high, I knew it was wrong and I hated myself, but I was not able to give up the drugs and alcohol. Twice I went into rehab but nothing worked. The draw of drugs eventually led to prostitution. I would do anything to get my fix. If it hadn't been for the Star Man, I would probably be dead today." She paused, took another bite of her Big Mac and ate some French fries. "Now I'm trying to make amends to all the people I wronged, but it's hard to face my family.

I've hurt them deeply and I don't know if they'll ever fully recover from my behavior."

"You mentioned that if it hadn't been for the Star Man that you'd probably be dead. Can you tell me about that?" I asked.

She nodded and sipped her Diet Coke.

"It happened almost two years ago. I had a dreadful day. I had gone to town in search of some Johns. I needed money in the worst way. Drugs are not cheap and I needed a fix. I earned about two hundred dollars and was going to head back to the reservation and get high when another client stopped me and offered me a fifty. Not one to turn down money, I got in his car and he drove me out in the country. I knew the area. I had gone there before on camping trips with my family. It was near a state park. Before I knew what was happening, he attacked me and beat me unconscious. Later I discovered that he raped me, stole my money and left me for dead."

"Did you report it?"

"That's not something you do around here. The white cops would've blamed me and thrown me in jail. When I became conscious, I started walking down the road. That's when I encountered the Star Man."

"Did you see a spacecraft?" I asked.

"No. He was just standing there in the middle of the road. There was a strange, blue brilliance about him. Almost a glow. I never really knew if it was the reflection of the moon or if it was a natural brilliance."

"Can you explain what you mean by brilliance?"

"It's very difficult to explain. It was more like neon than a glow. That's the reason I think it might have been a reflection, but I'm still not sure. You have to remember, at that time, I was almost beaten to death."

"So what did the Star Man do?"

"He told me not to be afraid. He said he was there to help me, but in return, I must change my life."

"How did he help you?"

"I remember a rushing stream that ran beside the road. He led me there and washed the blood from my face and hands. There was warmth to his touch despite the cold mountain water that he used. I know my face was bruised and battered, and I could barely see out of one of my eyes. He ran his hand over my face and, honest to God, I swear the swelling and pain went away. While he worked on my face, his hands glowed a bright orange. I hurt too much to resist and I just let him do his thing. Then he asked me to lie down in the grass by the stream. I obeyed."

"How were you communicating with him?" I asked.

"I think we just knew each other thoughts without talking."

"What did he do once you lay down?"

"He continued to run his hands over my body. When he reached a place where I had a lot of pain, he stopped for a moment and the pain went away."

She took another bite of her Big Mac and watched two well-dressed men stop at a table no more than ten feet from us. She took another sip of her Coke, got up, retrieved some ketchup, and returned to the table.

"I don't know those men, but I think we should be discreet," she said.

I moved around in my chair and looked at them. Other than wearing dark glasses in McDonalds and white shirts and ties, they might have passed for any tourist in the area.

"I've seen them before," she whispered. "Do you think they're following me?"

"I really don't know," I said, "but they look like Mormon missionaries or Jehovah Witnesses to me. I see them on reservations everywhere. Still trying to convert the Natives."

"I know you probably think I'm crazy, but I've seen those two men four times in the last two days. I saw them yesterday afternoon when I came out of class. They were sitting on the brick wall near the campus entrance. Then last night when I left the AA meeting, they were standing in the parking lot. This morning, I saw them walking down the block where I live and now tonight. I just don't think they are here by accident."

In an attempt to distract her, I continued my questioning. "You were telling me that the Star Man healed you with his hands. Can you tell me more about that?"

She nodded. "Once he located a place of pain, he hovered over the injured area with his hands. A hot, orange glow came from his hands. Soon the pain disappeared. The next day I went to the IHS [Indian Health Service]. The doctor told me that it appeared that I had four broken ribs, a broken bone in my right leg, and a broken pelvic bone. He couldn't believe that I had been injured in less than twelve hours. He said I was healing perfectly."

"So you're telling me the Star Man saved your life?"

"Yes. He saved my life."

"Can you describe the machine he was using?"

"There was no machine. Only his hands," she replied.

"After he healed you, what did he do?"

"He told me that he found strange substances in my blood and those substances were going to kill me, so he removed those, too."

"Are you telling me that once he healed you, you were no longer addicted to drugs and alcohol?"

"That's what I'm telling you. It was like I'd never used drugs. I felt strong and without any desire to find a dealer. The next day, I went to the tribal college and enrolled. I plan to study nursing, but I'm putting in my first two years at the tribal college so I can do some things to help my mom before I leave the reservation."

"After he healed you, can you tell me what happened?"

"He told me that he would check on me from time to time to make sure that I was healthy. He took me to the middle of the road, and I saw a blue ball move upward toward the heavens. I looked around me and I was standing at the reservation line. I walked home. When I appeared in the doorway, my mother looked at me and almost didn't recognize me. I never told her how I became sober. I go to AA because that's what she wants me to do, but I really don't need it. I'll never do drugs again."

I see Sylvia when I return to the reservation. Every time I visit, we have dinner at McDonalds and laugh about the two strangers who were "following" her. It turns out they were visiting Mormons on their mission. I had seen others like them before in their shirts and ties on the reservation, attempting to convert American Indians to their faith. Sylvia, who has a 4.0 grade point average at the tribal college, looks forward to attending the university next fall. I will miss our trips to McDonalds. She is not the first person I met who had been saved by the Blue Men, but she is certainly the first to tell me about being healed of a drug addiction. Perhaps there is hope for the world after all.

15. BETTY'S STORY:
THE SHINING MEN UNSTUCK ME

Betty worked for the U.S. Postal Service on the reservation. After a year of employment, she was put in charge of making sure that the rural delivery routes were covered. She often traveled the backroads of the reservation to deliver the mail when a rural deliverer called in sick. According to one of her friends, Betty reportedly had witnessed a number of UFOs during those trips. I went to the post office in search of Betty, hoping she would share with me her various sightings. This is Betty's story.

When I arrived at the post office, Betty was the only person staffing the counter. I watched as she handled the last customer, answered the phone, and searched for a lost package. When she turned her attention to me, I told her I heard that she reportedly had seen UFOs on the rural routes and wondered if she would be interested in talking with me. The petite woman with black curly hair and the energy of a dozen women wrote her address on a slip of paper and slid it across the counter. "Tomorrow is Saturday. I make pancakes on Saturday for my kids. Stop by and we will have coffee and talk."

The next morning, I took Betty up on her invitation and sat around the table with her three children as she stood at the stove making pancakes. Wearing jeans and a sweatshirt with the local high school mascot on the front, she offered up pancakes like a worker on an assembly line. The children, who were as energetic as their mother, peppered me with questions about college. The oldest, Benjamin, wanted to be a veterinarian. Mary Sue, the middle child, had already decided at the age of nine that she wanted to be a teacher. Her youngest, Tate, wanted to be firefighter. As I engaged in a lively conversation with the children, Betty moved about the kitchen with the efficiency of a woman accustomed to multitasking. Just as the children finished their breakfast, Betty's mother entered the kitchen, shook my hand, and welcomed me. When she sat down, Betty dutifully served her pancakes and coffee. After the breakfast dishes were in the sink, Betty's mother indicated she would do the cleanup duty, and Betty and I went into the living room with our coffee.

"It's fairly common knowledge that I see UFOs all the time," she said.

"Is there a particular area where they appear more often?"

"It's not news that UFOs fly over the reservation all the time. You could ask any ten people, and nine out of ten would tell you about seeing unexplainable things in the sky."

"I've heard you've had several sightings," I said.

"I've had more than I can count, but there is one in particular that changed my life." She paused and looked out the window at her children who were merrily playing in the snow in the front yard.

"Would you tell me about that?" I asked. She hesitated. "You know I write books about UFO encounters. I promise I will never use your name and I will disguise your location."

She looked at me, nodded, and let out a long sigh. "There was a blizzard that day. The carrier called in saying his car couldn't get out of his driveway due to drifting snow. It was snowing very hard. It was a long route and one that I dreaded. I remembered how I struggled to keep the windshield clear as the snow came down in huge flakes, making visibility limited. Twice I went off the road and had to shovel myself out."

"Were you stranded when you saw the UFO?" I asked.

She nodded. "I was on my way home. It was about 7 p.m., so it was very dark except for an occasional light from a ranch house. When I came around the hairpin curve at Wild Horse Butte, that's when I got the shock of my life. There was a light show in the sky.

It was beautiful. I saw five beautiful blue balls. I stopped my vehicle right in the middle of the road and sat there watching. Suddenly, the balls joined together into one ball and disappeared. I thought the light show was over. I put my car in gear and continued my trip home."

"Was there any interference with your car or radio during this time?"

"Nothing that I remember. My car was still running, and I was playing a CD of the old Indian rock group, XIT, that my kids made from the internet."

"Did anything else happen?" I asked.

"I hadn't driven a half mile, when all of a sudden, a huge, luminous ball of light appeared in front of me and came to rest on the road. There was no place for me to go. I couldn't go around it. There were four feet snow banks on each side of the road made by the snowplows. I couldn't drive through them. I put my car in reverse and stepped on the accelerator. All of a sudden, my car spun out of control. When I came to a stop, the car was in a barrow pit. I knew if someone didn't drive by, I'd be spending the night in my car. I thought about my children. They were home waiting for their mama, and I was stuck in a snow bank fifty miles from home."

"What about your cell phone?"

"Cell phones are useless in the rural areas on the reservation. When it comes to technology, reservations live in the dark ages even though this is the space age."

"Is the blue ball still on the highway at this time?" I asked.

"Not only is it there, but the blue light faded and I made out a large, round machine setting on the road. I realized it was a UFO. The bright blue lights were underneath the craft. It covered the whole road. It was about thirty feet high and covered both lanes of the road."

"How did you know it was a spacecraft?"

"What else could it be? It wasn't a plane or a helicopter. It was a huge circular craft. I knew it was a UFO. But that's not all.

As I sat there trying to decide my next step, I saw the outline of five shining blue figures. They appeared in human shape but the shimmering light was so bright that it distorted any features."

"What was your reaction?" I asked.

"I was scared to death. I reached in my glove compartment and pulled out my .22."

"A gun?"

"Yes. I had a little .22 handgun. I always carried it with me. It's not meant to kill, but I guess it could. It gives me that extra sense of safety."

"Were you planning to shoot the entities approaching you?" I asked.

"Not unless they planned to harm me. I wouldn't shoot to kill, but I'd aim at their legs. I'm a pretty good shot."

"Can you describe the shining Blue Men?"

"I'm trying to think of the word. Despite the shimmering blue light, I could make out a human form. They must be full of electricity. They looked human and they were walking toward me. I saw arms and legs and a head, but no features. The glowing lights were too bright."

"Can you describe anything else about them?"

"All I know is they looked like humans, I mean, they had the outline of humans."

"How tall were they?"

"Huge. Maybe about eight feet, maybe a few inches shorter. I really couldn't say."

"Could you tell how they were dressed?" I asked.

"They weren't dressed as I could tell. Just shimmering blue light."

"Did you ever fire your gun?"

"No." She sat quietly for a moment, got up, walked into the kitchen, and returned with the coffee pot. She refilled our cups.

"I don't know how to explain this. It was so strange and unbelievable."

"Simply tell me what happened," I said.

"As the entities approached, I cocked the gun. I don't know what I was thinking. In my head, I heard voices saying 'Do not be afraid. We will help.' I looked around trying to figure out who was talking, but there was no one there and yet, the entities kept coming toward me."

"What happened when they reached the car?" I asked.

"They never really reached it. About five feet away, they pointed their right, no left, arm at the car. The rear-end of the car suddenly moved upward. Then the car wobbled and shook and I was airborne. They raised my car into the air about six feet and stabilized it. For a moment, it was suspended in the air, and then suddenly the car moved up and up. I was terrified. I didn't know what was going to happen to me. But I kept hearing these voices saying 'Do not be afraid.'"

She got up and looked out the window at her children who were building a snow fort in the front yard. "My kids are my life," she continued. "That's all I thought about. Before I knew it, I was moving over the spacecraft, and then gently, they set my car down on the highway again. I couldn't believe it. I was unstuck from the snow bank by the shining men. I looked behind me for some sign of the five strangers, but I saw no one. I quickly started my car, stepped on the accelerator, and drove toward home, probably faster than I should have. I stopped for nothing, but I knew they were behind me."

"How did you know that?" I asked.

"From the blue lights reflecting in my mirrors."

"Did they follow you home?"

"They followed me until the lights of town appeared, and then they were gone. When the lights disappeared behind me, I relaxed. My back hurt, my arms hurt. When I pulled into my driveway, I sat there and cried. Eventually my mother opened the door and called to me."

"Did you tell her what happened?"

"I never told anyone before," she said.

"I heard you were quitting your job at the post office. Is it because of this encounter?"

"Yeah, I've submitted my notice. I'm going back to school to update my teaching credentials." Betty paused and took a drink of her coffee. "I'm still young enough that I can have a teaching career. I taught school a year before I came to the post office. I've decided to update my credentials."

"Was the experience so traumatic that it caused you to make these changes in your life?" I asked.

"Yes and no. I was tired of being responsible for the rural routes. I don't see that changing in the future. After fifteen years, I'm ready for a change. But the biggest factor may be what happened." Suddenly the door opened and three bouncing children came into the living room. As they all talked to her all at once about their snow fort, I saw a woman who listened to each child and responded. It was obvious she was devoted to them. When they left the room, she turned to me. "Knowing there is life outside Earth has made a big impression on me. I always knew it, but to encounter it is something else. It makes me worry about the future of my kids."

"Can you explain why you worry?" I asked.

"Okay. I know the ones I encountered were considerate of my situation. They followed me, maybe to make sure I got home safely. But in the back of my mind, I worry. What would have happened to me if they decided to abduct me? What if they weren't kind? Then what would happen to my children?"

She paused again and looked at me for an answer.

"I've heard many stories about UFO encounters and star people," I said. "And despite how unique or outrageous they may appear, I always keep faith that whatever awaits us in the future, I will be ready to step up."

She smiled. "You know, that's a good point."

I see Betty on a regular basis. She resigned from the post office, completed the coursework to renew her teaching certificate, and teaches second grade at the local elementary school. Her children are doing well and are always happy to see me. When I stay over on the weekends, I always join them for a pancake breakfast. Betty has never encountered the Star Men again, but she also admits she does not drive on rural roads after dark anymore.

16. KENNETH'S STORY: THE STAR MEN TAUGHT ME TO USE MY POWER

Kenneth was nineteen the first time he was visited by the Star People. At the time I spoke with him, he was sixty-eight and the visits had not ceased. The owner of a convenience store and gas station combo on the reservation, he remained a bachelor all of his life. A leader in the traditional religious community, Kenneth often talked about the importance of remembering the old ways, telling the legends, and practicing the religion. He frequently held ceremonies both on and off the reservation. I met him at a pow wow in Bozeman, Montana. He had traveled far to conduct a sweat lodge ceremony. I had been invited to participate. During the ceremony, small balls of light entered the lodge. Kenneth told us not to fear. The Star People were visiting us. Later, I asked him about the Star People. He invited me to visit him on the reservation where we could talk.

On my next trip to the reservation, I stopped at a bakery and special ordered a box of fruitcake cupcakes. I scheduled my trip so I would arrive on Saturday night and meet Kenneth on Sunday at a prearranged time. When I arrived at his home, he was standing in the doorway waiting for me. He welcomed me into his home and immediately opened his gift. I watched the smile on his face when he opened the box.

"You are a woman after my heart," he said as he offered a fruitcake cupcake to me and chose one for himself. "Someone told you I love fruitcake. I made a pot of fresh coffee. So let's enjoy." I looked at the man who had lived seven decades as he walked to the stove and picked up his coffee pot. His long, black hair was parted in the middle and fell to his shoulders. His piercing brown eyes and his striking smile set off his face, which was mostly wrinkle-free. Red suspenders held up his beltless, tan work pants. A red and black buffalo checked flannel shirt, which was too big for his small frame, was stuffed neatly inside his pants. I watched as he poured two cups of coffee, offered me a paper towel as a napkin, and meticulously removed the wrapper from the cupcake.

"You are the first person to ask me about the Star People," he began after taking a bite of the fruitcake. "When I perform a ceremony, the Star People are always with me. They frequently come into the sweat lodge and participate."

"Can you explain to me how they participate?"

"They enter the sweat lodge and touch the participants. In some cases, they assist with a healing. They are always with me."

"When I was in your sweat lodge, I saw the small balls of light. Were those the Star People?"

"Yes. They come in many forms, but sparks of light, balls of light are common. They can also take human form. But in the sweats, they mostly appear as light."

"Tell me about the first time you saw them."

"I was in the military. This was back in the days when the draft was in place, and after I graduated high school, I joined the Marines. I was proud to serve my country. I arrived in country in 1965. I was nineteen at the time. We were sent there to secure U.S. airbases, but we ended up in combat operations instead of defensive force. After that, the war escalated and the rest is history."

"You said your first encounter was while you were in the military. Did it happen in Vietnam?"

"I was a gunner on a helicopter. We would fly into the Delta to pick up fellow Marines. My job was to protect my comrades as they boarded the helicopter, among other things. On one occasion, there were several wounded. Those who were not wounded were having difficulty getting the wounded to the helicopter. I jumped out to help when the helicopter came under heavy fire. The pilot had no choice but to leave. I tried to move the wounded to a more secure location with the help of two other marines."

He paused, went to the counter, and retrieved a second cupcake. He refilled his cup of coffee and offered to refill mine. After he sat down again, he continued. "This next part is unbelievable, but I swear it did happen. All of a sudden, it was like we were in a bubble. I could still hear the gunfire, but it was like it was in the distance. We were suddenly bathed in a bright light and we were taken upward. At the time I had no idea what was happening. There was no helicopter, but we appeared to be in a transport of some kind. Then, we were on the ground again, and the helicopter was approaching. There was no gunfire. We loaded the wounded onto the copter, and we were flown to safety. It was like for one moment the war stopped."

"You said there were two others who were not wounded. Did they remember anything?"

"Nothing. They had no idea that the event occurred."

"Now that you think about it, what do you think happened?"

"I don't know. After I returned to the states and made my way home, I put the event behind me. I got married to a wonderful young woman, who was more patient with me than she should have been. I kept having flashbacks to that moment. I never slept through the night. Finally, we both agreed the marriage was not good and she left. I moved out here and built this cabin. It's where I belong."

"When did you realize it was an intervention by the Star People?"

"After my wife left, I did a lot of soul searching. One night, I built a fire in the backyard pit, which I do most nights, and I saw my first UFO. As I watched, captivated by the sight, the craft descended slowly and landed in the field to the south. Two figures approached me. They told me not to be afraid. I tried to stand, but I was too weak to move. They said that we had met before. Then they revealed that they had saved me in Vietnam."

"Were they talking about the event that occurred on the ground?"

"Yes. They proceeded to tell me that they saved me for a

purpose."

"A purpose?"

"They said I was destined to be a healer among the people. They would help me. I had to forget the war and make something positive out of my life. Then they were gone."

"Can you describe your visitors?"

"I never saw them in full light the first time they came, but the next time, they took me on board their craft and that's when I saw them."

"Can you describe them?"

"They were tall, maybe as tall as seven feet. They were very muscular. They shimmered. Their skin was light blue."

"Light blue?"

"The shimmering light around them was blue, but their skin appeared a lighter shade of blue. They were peaceful souls who traveled the world and healed pain. They taught me to channel their energy and to use my own energy to heal. We all have that ability but do not use our power. The star men taught me how to use my power and to tune into theirs. They changed my life. I'm no longer the man that came back from Vietnam. I'm not the boy that joined the Marines. I'm a healer."

"Do the Blue Men frequently visit you?"

"They are always with me. If I'm in the sweat lodge, if I'm called to pray for someone, if I'm alone in my cabin, their presence is always with me. They healed my PTSD. I am not the man who came back from 'Nam. I am thankful for them."

"Do the Blue Men appear in different forms to you?"

"They can appear in solid form, but they are mostly balls of energy. You saw them in the sweat lodge in Bozeman. Because they are energy, they prefer that form."

I have seen Kenneth since our meeting and make sure that he gets a box of fruitcake cupcakes when I do. Mostly I hear about a miracle healing he has performed. While I have not seen the Marine who suffered from PTSD, I have seen the gentle, caring man that he is today and don't question his story that the Blue Men are the ones responsible for his transformation.

SECTION 2

REPTILIANS AND INSECTOIDS

1. REPTILIANS AND INSECTOIDS: INTRODUCTION

Many UFO eyewitnesses have described reptilians over the last several decades. Descriptions range from beings who stand six-to-nine-feet tall with long torsos to lizard-like creatures with tails. Some observers report they have three fingers with a thumb; others said they have four-to-six-digit, claw-like hands. Some describe dark brown or green scales for skin; others report a smoother skin with a sheen that changes color from dark green to brown with movement. A few of the witnesses claim they had long, forked tongues and emit a stinging, poisonous venom.

One of the earliest alien abduction narratives came from police officer Herbert Schirmer who alleged that he was taken aboard a UFO by humanoid beings with reptilian features.

David Icke, a conspiracy theorist, claims that reptilians have taken human form and control Earth by infiltrating governments, banking, businesses, and even royal families. Stewart Swerdlow describes the activities of a reptilian race called the Draco, who come from the Draco star system. Zecharia Sitchin, an archaeologist, author, and linguist, claims that an ancient race of extraterrestrials, the Anunnaki, genetically engineered the original humans. He further maintained these beings were reptilian, quasi-reptilian, or amphibious.

John Carpenter, an alien abduction researcher, describes the reptilians as having faces like snakes. Their eyes have golden or purple irises with vertical slits and their hands are webbed. He states that they were a highly intelligent race with well-developed telepathy, which they used as mind control. He maintains they were among the most feared species in the universe. Thomas Castello, a former Dulce base security technician, claims that Dulce was a secret base operated in New Mexico by humans as well as reptilian aliens and their worker class, the Greys. According to Castello, genetic experiments on kidnapped men, women, and children were carried out in this secretive base.

Several ancient cultures described reptilian beings. One story of note was an Athabasca legend of a cannibalistic, lizard-like tribe of men with tails who preyed upon the local villagers. Some legends identified the reptilians as stone-like creatures. More often than not, they were hostile to humans. The Hopi described a race of reptilians called the *Sheti*, or "Snake-Brothers," who lived underground. The Maya spoke of a reptilian race, often called the "Iguana-Men," who descended from the sky. According to Cherokee legend, the great warrior *Aganunitsi* killed *Uktena*, described as a lizard-snake like monster and brought back the shining seventh scale from his chest, which resembles a large, transparent crystal with a blood-red streak and possesses mysterious powers. In Colombia, Bachue (the primordial woman) transformed into a big snake and was called the "Celestial Snake."

Reptile creatures are not the only unique life forms described by abductees. Some abductees have encountered Insectoid beings. The term Insectoid denotes any creature or object that shares a body or traits similar to common insects. Mantis-like, ant-like, or bug-like beings are among the many different types reported as being seen during abductions working alongside other alien types. Some are said to be kind and humble; others are described as aggressive.

Descriptions of these entities often include such features as long, narrow faces with slanted eyes, and long torsos with thin arms usually crooked into a sharp bend at the mid-joint. The legs are also bent at an almost right angle at the mid-joint creating a crouched position.

Insects play a wide variety of different roles in the legends of Native American tribes. They often appear in legends to symbolize meekness and humility, two positive traits valued by most American

Indian cultures. One of the most intriguing legends involves the Hopi and the Ant People, who were crucial to the survival of the Hopi in both the "First World" and "Second World." During the destruction of each world, virtuous members of the Hopi tribe were guided by the sky god, *Sotuknang*, who took them to the Ant People, *Anu Sinom*. The Ant People escorted the Hopi into subterranean caves where they found refuge and sustenance. The Ant People were portrayed as generous and industrious, giving the Hopi food when supplies ran short and taught them the merits of food storage. One legend stated the reason why ants have such thin waists today was because they once deprived themselves of provisions in order to feed the Hopi.

In this section, you will read about encounters with both Reptilians and Insectoids. While some of the experiences were positive, they were more likely to be negative.

2. CLINTON'S STORY: A SPACE-AGE INDIAN AND STAR LIZARDS

I met Clinton through his cousin who served on the BIA Police Force. Clinton had trained to be a police officer, but after his training he decided to open his own security company on the reservation. He had a cadre of young men located throughout the reservation who worked for him. While his firm had clients from the business community, most of his business came from individuals who wanted their houses patrolled when they were out of town on business or on vacation. According to his cousin, Clinton told him of an encounter with three monstrous aliens on one of his routine patrols. Clinton agreed to meet me for a late lunch at the local reservation cafe to tell me about his encounter.

When I arrived at the cafe, I recognized Clinton immediately. He was sitting in a back booth staring at the menu. From my vantage point, I could tell he was a tall man, as his legs were stretched out into the aisle. His black hair was cut in a short, military style. The outline of his muscles showing through his tight-fitting black t-shirt indicated he was in good shape. When I approached, he stood. He smiled shyly as I introduced myself. He waited until I was seated in the booth before he sat down. Within seconds, the waitress appeared and told us the kitchen would be closing in preparation for dinnertime in a few minutes and we needed to order right away. We ordered and she left after bringing us water.

"I don't know what my cousin told you," Clinton began in a low voice.

"Not much, only that you had a terrifying encounter, and he thought if you talked to me, I might be able to help you put everything into perspective." He nodded and watched the waitress place two ice teas on the table.

"I don't trust her," Clinton whispered. "She's always eavesdropping on my conversations. She will be gone in a few minutes and then we can talk more freely."

I nodded. When the waitress returned with our lunch, Clinton sized up the Indian taco and began cutting it with his knife and fork.

"I don't know where to start," he said.

"Just start at the beginning," I said encouraging him. He took a bite of his taco, a sip of his tea, and began.

"It was a subzero night in January when I got a call from Joe, one of my guys who works on the east side of the reservation. He said he was sick and unable to patrol several unoccupied houses on his rounds." Clinton shuffled his feet and moved sideways as the waitress approached. She brought a pitcher of ice tea and advised us she was going off-duty and needed to be paid. Clinton reached for his billfold, handed her a twenty, and told her to keep the change.

"I didn't have anyone to cover for Joe," he continued, "so I decided, despite the distance of fifty miles, I would cover for him and get one of my in-town guys to cover for me. It was a long drive. The heater on my pickup was on the blitz, and my windshield kept fogging up with ice crystals. I had a bottle of anti-freeze behind my seat, and I stopped periodically and poured the fluid across the glass. I remember it was below zero, and twenty miles into the drive I wished I'd stayed in town."

"How long did it take you to arrive at your destination?"

"It was nearly two hours. Not having a heater was the biggest problem, and the snow-covered roads had turned to ice. When I arrived at the driveway of the first house on my round, my pickup suddenly lost power. The driveway was about a quarter mile long. So I checked my flashlight and started the long trek to the house."

"What happened to your truck?" I asked.

"I don't know. It just quit. The lights went out, the radio

stopped, and the engine died."

"But your flashlight worked, correct?"

"Yes, but I didn't need it. There was a full moon, and once my eyes adjusted to the night without the headlights, I was able to see quite well. As I walked up the driveway, the house and barn set at the top of a small hill, I saw a light toward the back of the house."

"Can you describe the light?"

"It was a powerful light, shining a wide beam. I thought it was a burglar with a flashlight. Then I saw another light and then another. There were three of them. Fortunately, I had my revolver. I pulled it out of my holster and decided to creep around the opposite side of the house to get a drop on them."

"Do you always carry a firearm?" I asked.

"Usually. I have a legal carry permit from the tribe, which allows me to defend myself, although I've never used it. This night was different."

"Did you find your burglars?"

"When I reached the house, I crept along the side, hoping to surprise them. Just as I planned to get the jump on them, their flashlights turned toward me, blinding me. I knew they were advancing on me as the spotlights moved in my direction. I raised my gun and ordered them to stop. I no sooner got it out of my mouth than I felt a hand on my neck."

He paused and finished off his glass of ice tea.

"Was it one of the burglars?" I asked.

"This wasn't a burglar. Look at me. I'm a big guy. I am six feet four and weigh two-hundred-and-forty pounds. I work out and bench press three hundred pounds. But whatever had a hold of my neck lifted me off the ground like I was a toy. I couldn't see who or what it was, and the more I struggled, the more my assailant squeezed my neck. I finally gave up, and once I relented, I saw the faces of the others. They were not human. I don't know what they were, but they were not human."

"What happened when you saw them?"

"They were communicating among themselves. I think that's

what their grunts and whistles, almost like hisses, were. Then suddenly my assailant in the back picked me up, threw me over his shoulder, and walked toward the darkness. That's when I saw the ground shimmering with light. I couldn't tell where it came from, but I was surprised at the light. Then I became aware that this monster was carrying me up some sort of ramp. He carried me inside a structure and locked me in a room. I was alone in a dimly lit place no bigger than a bathroom. I searched for an exit, but the walls were strange like sponge, porous and wet with no evidence of a door. There was no escape. I no longer had my gun. I don't know what happened to it. I had nothing to defend myself."

"Was there anything else about the room that you remember?"

"Just a dim light filtering down. I ran my hands along the walls. They were warm and smelled like swamp water. When I banged on the walls, it left imprints, but they quickly disappeared."

"How long were you in this room?" I asked.

"I have no idea. Maybe a half hour. I know it was not long until I had the sensation that we were airborne. There were no windows and I could not confirm my suspicions, but a few minutes later one of them came in and took me into another room. There was a viewing center in one corner, and I watched as the Earth faded away. It was then that I realized that I was in far more trouble than I could have imagined."

"Can you describe the creatures that abducted you?" I asked.

"They were huge, scaly, figures with flat faces, big wide mouths. They looked like lizards. They must have stood eight feet tall. I felt like a dwarf next to them. They wore no clothes, although they had some kind of belt around their waist. They had flashlights and what I assumed were weapons strapped to their arms. And their arms were huge. Twice the size of my leg and they possessed tremendous strength. Their eyes, they were the scariest part of all. Huge oval-shaped eyes that wrapped partially around the sides of their heads. Their pupils were yellow and oval-shaped."

"Were there any other creatures in the room at this time?"

"No. I was just deposited in this room with the viewing center, and again, I was unable to find my way out. To tell you the truth, I never expected to see Earth again."

"So what happened?"

"I don't know. The next thing I remember. I was lying outside my client's house. My pants and shirt were gone. I was in subzero weather without any clothes but my underwear. I was freezing. I ran to my vehicle. I had left the keys inside when I walked up the driveway. That saved my life. I managed to turn around and make it back to town."

"How were you able to do that with no heater in your car?"

"I had an old hunting coat in the pickup. I put it on, but the strangest thing happened when I started up the engine—the heater suddenly came on. Before long, I was warm. When I got to town, I headed for the IHS [Indian Health Hospital]. I was lucky that there was no one else in the waiting room. The doctor on call examined me and asked about the claw marks on the back of my neck."

"What did you tell him?" I asked.

"I told them I got tangled up in some briars while hunting. He looked strangely at me, put some antiseptic on it, took a few stitches, and released me. He gave me a pair of doctor's pants."

"Did he ask you about your clothes?"

"I told him I lost them in a poker game." Clinton smiled and looked at me.

"Do you really think he believed that?"

He shrugged. "The ER sees lots of strange characters at night. If he didn't believe me, he said nothing."

"Did you have any other injuries?" I asked.

"Bruises, but no significant injuries other than my neck. When I got home, I fell into bed. I kept having all kinds of nightmares about the creatures."

"Can you describe your dreams?"

"I don't remember much. I kept waking up every time the dream got too unbearable. All I know is that they did things to me. Things I don't want to think about. And why? Why would they do this to me? Or to any human? We don't think that lizards could have these kinds of brains, or fly in a spaceship. But these ones did. It makes a man think, what other kinds of creatures are out there landing on this planet? We are like babies to them as far as advances in space travel. And what were they doing at an old ranch house on an Indian reservation? It makes no sense. Nothing makes sense. In Sunday School, the teachers taught us that God made man in his image." He paused and looked at me as if waiting for a response. "I mean, this is the space age. Isn't the idea that we evolved?" he asked.

"Maybe God made other intelligent beings too, just not in His image."

He nodded. "That's probably it. God made them, too."

"Did you have any other marks?" I asked.

"None that I noticed. My neck is another story. It's painful every day. I can't work like I used to, and my fitness program has taken a back seat. What do you think they wanted with me?"

"All I can tell you is that you are not the first person to tell me about encounters with lizard-like people. And as in your case, most of them can be quite aggressive. Let me ask you this, did you ever go out to the site where it happened?"

"The very next day. I measured the footprints around the house. They were twenty-four-inches long and six-inches wide. I found one that looked more like a claw print. But the sun had come out and was melting the snow. I found the spot where the spacecraft landed. All the snow was gone. There was an elongated spot with a semi-circle at the front. I measured it. It was nearly one-hundred feet from end to end. I assumed that was the length of the craft."

"Did you take any photos?"

"Never thought to take a camera, and my phone is a simple TracFone. No photo capabilities. I'm not into smartphones. I don't need somebody tracking me all the time. I keep things simple."

"And your gun?"

"I found my gun and flashlight up against the house, probably where I dropped it. Funny thing though, the gun was useless. It was like something very hot had melted the firing mechanism. I took it to a gun dealer in the city, and he said it was beyond repair. Although he said he'd never seen anything like it, he offered me seventy-five dollars toward a new one if I'd give it to him. I took the deal, but a few hours later, I got to thinking that someday it might be important, so I went back to the gun dealer, but he refused to return it to me."

"Anything else?"

"Nothing I can remember. It sure made me rethink my occupation. After that, I decided to go back to college and become a teacher. I don't want to be responsible for the same thing happening to my guys [his employees], and I sure don't want to go through that again. The tribe is considering buying my business. That would be good for me. I could go to school without borrowing money."

"Anything else?"

"Yeah, when I go out at night, I stay away from isolated places. I never leave home without a handgun and generally with a friend. I think there is safety in numbers." He laughed and scooted sideways in the booth, stretched his legs into the aisle, and then looked at me pensively. "I have a lot of trouble with my neck. It hurts like hell every day. By the evening, I'm on heating pads. Chiropractors and doctors haven't helped. Guess that's my souvenir from my encounter."

"Do you have scars from the ordeal?" I asked. He turned around so that his back was facing me. He pulled down the collar of his shirt, and I saw the large white scars across his neck. They reminded me of a bear mauling victim I once met in northern Montana. Even if he had wanted to forget about that night, his scars and pain were a constant reminder.

I have seen Clinton a few times since he told me his story. He is now a junior at the state university. He is studying to be a math teacher. He has had no further encounters, but the memory is ever-present in his mind. He still has trouble with his neck and admits that he has to limit his time on the computer, despite the fact that many of his courses require him to go online. There is no question that Clinton's encounter with the star lizards changed the direction of his life and his health as well. For Clinton, his encounter did not have a positive outcome.

3. JULIAN'S STORY: THE BUGGERS AND A TEEN-AGE PROSTITUTE

Julian was a former Bureau of Indian Affairs (BIA) police detective. As a federal officer, he was often temporarily posted at various reservations throughout the west. After leaving the service, he returned to his home reservation. He told me that during his years as a detective his investigations took him to many remote areas. Over the years, he had witnessed many UFOs, but nothing compared to the night he encountered a being on a desert road in Arizona.

In 2013, I received an email from Julian requesting an audience with me. He explained that he had read my book *Encounters with Star People*, and that it inspired him to tell his story. We agreed to meet in a small town near the Montana/South Dakota border for the interview. We scheduled to meet at a restaurant in a Best Western motel. When I arrived, there was no one in the restaurant. As the snow fell harder and harder, I decided it was likely he was delayed. I checked with the motel clerk for the latest weather report, and storm warnings had been issued for most of Montana and South Dakota. While I originally planned to drive to Billings that night, I decided to register at the motel and wait out the storm.

Three hours later, the clerk called my room and told me that Julian was waiting in the lobby of the motel.

When I entered the lobby, I immediately saw Julian, who was sitting in front of the fireplace watching a local weather report on TV. He stood as I approached and held out his hand. "It looks like our timing couldn't have been worse. I'm sorry you drove all this way to get stranded in a blizzard."

"Think nothing of it. It's winter and everyone knows that it can be sunny one hour and a blizzard the next. That's part of living in this part of the world."

"I know. But still, I feel bad that you're here and have to spend the night."

"I wasn't planning on driving home anyway. I was going to spend the night in Billings and drive home the next day. I changed my schedule and decided to spend the night here. It's not a problem." I saw him relax slightly and take a deep breath.

"I think I'd better register, too, before the motel is full. It doesn't look like anyone will be traveling tonight. Would you be willing to join me for dinner?" We agreed to meet at 6 p.m. in the motel dining room.

When we entered the restaurant, it was empty. We requested a private table and the hostess led us to a small table next to the window in the back of the dining room. As we looked over the menu, I noticed that Julian, who was dressed in a suit and tie, gave the impression of a professional man despite his boyish appearance. He wore a wedding band on his left hand and a turquoise nugget bracelet on his right wrist. At thirty-eight, he could have passed for at least ten years younger.

"You said in your emails that you were often temporarily detailed to different reservations," I said.

"That's typical of the BIA. They are short-handed, and when you become their employee, they can send you anywhere. That's one reason I left. I was always away from home."

"Which area of the country did you see the most UFOs?" I asked.

"That's difficult to say. Just about anytime I found myself on an isolated section of the reservation, and by that I mean one that was removed from a town. The sightings were similar in number, but the more isolated a reservation, the more UFO activity. The size of the reservation was another factor. The larger reservations seemed to have more remote areas where the UFOs could land and carry out their activities."

"What kind of activities?"

"Despite what everyone thinks, UFOs do land. They land to carry out maintenance, check their crafts for damage, and collect water. Scientists stop to collect soil, plants, seeds, and sometimes animals. Others stop to collect human beings. Most of the people they return; some they don't."

"You speak with the wisdom of someone who knows these things to be true. Do you have firsthand knowledge of these events?"

"I do." He paused as the waiter returned, filled our water glasses, and poured Julian a fresh cup of coffee. I eyed the man who sat across from me. He was articulate, methodical, and assured.

"How many UFOs have you seen in Indian country?" I asked.

"Dozens and dozens. They come in all forms. Some are balls of light. I discovered that the smaller balls of light are actually exploratory craft that scope out areas for inhabitants, privacy, and isolation. They return to the larger craft when they have completed their mission."

"Are those craft manned craft?" I asked.

"Some are one-man crafts; others, I believe, are remote controlled and are simply exploratory craft. It depends on the species. The reptile men use no exploratory craft. They have one purpose in mind and that is to kidnap victims and do their horrendous experiments. They are more malevolent than the Greys, but since their visits may result in the death of the abductees, no one really knows how often they visit Earth. Just another runaway or an unfortunate who probably was a victim of homicide, when the truth is they were victims all right, but victims of creatures from another world. The Greys are interested in reproduction."

"Do you think the technological age has changed their methods of collecting data?"

"It's funny you should ask that. The internet has changed a lot of things. People can now photograph their craft and put photos online. Of course, the government keeps denying they exist. They claim them as anomalies."

"Have you had experience with different species?"

"Yes," he said as he pushed back in his chair as the waiter delivered our steak dinners. After asking the waiter to bring steak sauce, he looked seriously at me and said. "No one knows the scope and frequencies of these visits. I don't think the government even knows, and reports of such events are just stored away in some big computer somewhere with little or no investigation."

"Do you think the government is complicit with alien groups?"

"I think there is a strong possibility, although I've been told by the beings themselves that they have perfected technology that allows them to come and go as they please unnoticed by our radar."

"Have you ever seen humans working with aliens?" I asked.

"Only once, and I didn't know if they were clones or humans."

"Do you think they prefer reservations or simply rural areas?"

"I don't know if they choose Indian reservations per say. I believe they are probably landing in remote areas all over the country. It is just that they are seen on the reservations more often because Indians are more aware of their environment."

"Can you explain that?" I asked.

"Indians have a long history of involvement with Star People. Our legends tell our history. And almost every reservation I have visited, when I talked with elders, they speak of interaction with the Star People. So when someone sees a UFO or encounters a star traveler, they are more likely to accept it and keep quiet about the event. Secondly, Indians like their privacy. So even though an area appears unpopulated, Indians have scattered themselves all across isolated sections of the reservations, so seeing a UFO or encountering a star man is more likely to occur. But I don't think it just happens on reservations."

"What do you mean?"

"I suspect it's no different in white America for those who live in remote areas. It's just that rural America doesn't have anyone seeking out the stories of those individuals like you have with Indians. Although there may be one difference. I think some of the tribes, and maybe all those that are more pure in blood, have

DNA that might be more compatible with alien blood."

"When you speak of pure in blood, do you mean full bloods versus those who are part Indian as determined by blood quantum?"

He nodded.

"From what I can gather, you have had multiple encounters. Am I correct?" I asked.

He nodded again.

"If you could choose one, the most significant one, which one would it be?"

He took the last bite of his steak and took a drink of his coffee. "I think it would be the reptilians. There are three species—the reptilians, the buggers, and the Grasshoppers or Mantis-men—they are the biggest threat to humanity."

"Who are you calling the buggers?"

"They are the insect guys"

"Have you ever read Orson Scott Card's *Ender's* books?" I asked.

He shook his head.

"Why?" he asked.

"Card called his fictional aliens, buggers."

"Well, maybe Orson Scott Card encountered them, too. I call them buggers because they look like monstrous bugs with rounded bodies and grasshopper legs. They stand upright to about seven feet tall and sometimes drop to the floor and sit on their haunches like grasshoppers. I saw them with the Greys, but the Greys do their bidding. The buggers are the ones in control, and they are scary dudes." He paused, emptied his coffee cup, and signaled the waiter for a refill. "Maybe I should call them boogers." We both laughed. "They sure could pass for boogie men."

"Can you tell me about them?" I asked.

"Aside from their formidable size, they have arms and legs with several joints. At each joint, there are long hairs maybe four inches long. They are like wild hairs in a beard. It is the only place I saw hair on their bodies. Their unusual joints allow them to manipulate things like a juggling act in a circus. They have long torsos, rounded middles, and long necks. Their faces are very strange. They're shaped like a big triangle with rounded edges, with these huge, slanted, black eyes. Their chins come to a sharp point."

"And their skin? Do they have scales like a fish or lizard?"

"No, not scales. They are nothing like fish or lizards. I've seen the lizard men. These creatures are different. Their skin is a combination of light green and tan. They actually appear to have a protective shell about their middle, similar to a beetle."

"Can you tell me about your first encounter with them?"

"I was on a reservation in the Southwest. I had been investigating a drug cartel that reportedly had encroached onto the reservation. I had a tip of a drug house where the drugs were processed and distributed. I was on my way to the address when I suddenly saw a tall creature on the edge of the highway. As I got closer, I couldn't believe my eyes. It looked like a giant grasshopper. I moved to the center of the highway and slowed to get a better look. I had a spotlight in my car, and I shined it toward the creature. I saw it crouch down, and when it stood again it was a human."

"Are you telling me it was a shapeshifter?"

"Yes. I knew I was in the presence of something not from this world. I have to admit it was unsettling. I stepped on the accelerator. I wanted to get out of there as quickly as possible, but the car came to a dead stop. I turned the key in the ignition, but there was no power."

"What did you do?"

"I wore a chest holster. I reached for my gun, but I couldn't move. The next thing I know, a human-like creature was leading me off the side of the road. I was worried about my car sitting in the middle of the road. He told me not to worry. He would take care of my car. I don't remember anything else until I was on board their spacecraft."

"What happened once you were on the craft?"

"I don't know how long they kept me there or how long I was unconscious. I know I lost about three-and-a-half hours of time. When my captor entered the room where I was kept, he was still in human form."

"I demanded to know where I was and if he had changed from an insect to a human appearing creature. I had had a previous experience with shapeshifting creatures and I knew their abilities."

"How did he react to that?"

"He didn't. At that moment, two small grey beings entered the room, and he grunted at them."

"Grunted?"

"I don't know. It was a strange clicking or grunting sound. Anyway, they moved to the back of the room and stood there like little soldiers."

"Can you describe the Greys?"

"They were exactly as they have been described by others. About four feet tall with big heads and eyes like the buggers, but small and skinny. They looked more human than the buggers but they weren't. They have the tiniest legs and their arms were longer than their legs. They had an ash color skin."

"Did the bugger ever communicate with you?" I asked.

"Yes. I asked him again why he had taken the form of a human, and he said it was to put me at ease. I was confused by that statement since he didn't seem to care about my feelings when he kidnapped me."

"Did he indicate why you needed to be at ease?"

"I think it was because he wanted to ask me questions. He asked the strangest questions. He asked me about my job! Can you believe that? He wanted to know why I captured people and put them in cages. I was absolutely floored by that."

"How did he know what you did?"

"I asked him the same question. He said they visited this planet frequently and this particular place on the reservation. He said they had followed my movements and were interested in what I did with the people I captured."

"Did you tell them about your profession?"

"I tried to explain. He seemed very confused. He told me that there was no need to put people in cages; there were other methods. Then he ordered the Greys forward and they grasped me by the arm and marched me behind him down a hallway. We came to a room that smelled like a hospital. There I met humans, or at least they looked human, but they were motionless. They looked awake, but they were in a trance-like state. They didn't speak, blink their eyes, or move the slightest."

"Why do you think he took you to this room?"

"I think it was his way of showing me that he could control individuals without jails."

"Do you remember anything else about the room?"

"One very important thing happened. He asked me how I would go about identifying the individuals I captured. I explained to him about fingerprints. I took my fingerprint pad out of my breast pocket, took the hand of one of the transfixed female captives, and pressed her thumb into it. I carefully transferred the print to a small notebook in my breast pocket. I showed it to him. I explained I could use the print from her thumb to identify the person. He seemed interested in the process. When he was distracted, I slipped the notebook back into my pocket and kept thinking about Christmas."

"Christmas?"

"Yes. I was planning to go home in two days to spend Christmas with my wife and children. I visualized the Christmas tree and opening presents."

"Why did you do that?"

"I knew he could read my mind. I didn't want to think about the notebook."

"How many humans did you see?"

"There were six. Three females and three males. They appeared to be in their twenties. Handsome men and beautiful women."

"How long did you stay in the room with the humans?"

"Not long. After that, the two Greys took me back to the holding room. I kept thinking of our Christmas tree from last year. I focused on seeing it in my mind. I didn't allow my mind to stray. Maybe an hour later, the bugger came back. He escorted me through the woods to my car and that was the end."

"What do you think they were doing with the humans?"

"I have no idea, but I don't think they were up to any good."

"Are you sure they were humans?"

"Yes, they were humans."

"How can you be so positive?"

"The notebook. I was able to lift a perfect fingerprint off the note paper. I put it in the IAFIS and I got a hit. A positive ID."

"What is the IAFIS?"

"It's the Integrated Automated Fingerprint Identification System maintained by the FBI. It also provides criminal history of the individuals in the system."

"Were you able to identify the individual?"

"Yes. She was a seventeen-year-old female from Las Vegas. She had been arrested four times for prostitution. She disappeared three years ago. Her roommate reported her missing. She said the last time she saw her, she was getting into a car with a strange looking man who was driving a Cadillac. She had no known living relatives. The police suspected she had either left the state or had met with foul play."

"Was there a photo?"

"Yes, and it was the same girl."

"What do you think they were doing with the humans?"

"I have no idea, but I don't expect their future is too promising. They are probably used for experiments because the room I was in had several strange looking machines that looked like hospital equipment. They apparently have a way of putting them in a trance state so they can keep them alive."

"How have you coped with this experience?" I asked.

"It has personally been devastating. I can't get that young woman out of my mind. She doesn't deserve this. I can't do anything about it. I couldn't report it. And the worst part, I couldn't warn other young people to be careful. Especially those with no one who really cared."

"Is that why you left the BIA?" I asked.

"I thought about her day and night. I left the BIA to get away from being assigned to isolated areas of the country. I stayed close to home. I wanted to make sure my family was safe, but at the same time I knew that if they wanted my daughters, they could take them and I would be powerless to stop them."

I have not seen Julian since his interview. During our meeting over that snow bound weekend, he told me about other encounters with star beings in New Mexico, Montana, Utah, South Dakota, Mississippi, North Carolina, and Oklahoma, but he felt this encounter was the most important. He wanted to share it as a warning to teenagers and young adults. As promised, I have included it. It is my hope that if you read it, you will heed his warning and keep your daughters and sons close to you.

4. ANNIE'S STORY: THE RETURN OF THE SHADOW STEALERS

Annie was a member of the reservation's Homeland Security Team (HST). She originally trained to be a police officer, but when the opportunity came to join the HST, she immediately took the job. At twenty-six and a college graduate, she hoped that this position might lead to advancement, which she viewed as unlikely in the police force. The HST responded to various events and emergencies on the reservation, including drug smuggling, illegal aliens, and as backup for the police department when they were overtaxed. One night, Annie took a call from a woman who was hysterical, saying that aliens had arrived on her property. Annie and her partner Eric responded to the call and encountered a situation that was out of this world.

I met Annie at the defunct civil defense office on the reservation. It had been set up in the 1950s and from all indications had not been used since then. At the encouragement of the tribal chairman, Annie took it upon herself to clear out the space to make way for the headquarters of the Homeland Security Team. When I entered the building, I called out and she yelled back. I followed her voice and found her lining up three chairs around a table.

"This is my partner, Eric," she said as I walked into the room. "I invited him to join us since he witnessed the event. I thought if I left anything out, he could fill in."

I nodded and dug in my bag for the tape recorder. Eric grabbed Cokes from the hallway beverage machine and placed them on the table. The two of them sat across the table from me.

"Eric, did you lock the door?" Annie asked. Eric got up to check. "I don't want anyone walking in on us," she explained.

I nodded again. Annie was strikingly beautiful. Her long black hair was upswept into a bun on the back of head, revealing her flawless skin and black eyes. She appeared rather petite for her job description, but her partner Eric looked like he was quite capable to taking care of both of them. Eric was equally as attractive as Annie. A graduate of a prestigious engineering college, he was in a similar situation. Unable to find a job in his field, he returned home to live with his mother and took the first job that became available. As a result, the two misplaced college graduates found themselves as the Homeland Security Team.

"Anne, you told me that you and Eric had an amazing experience one night when you received a call for help. Could you tell me about it?"

"It had been a quiet night," she began. "I was home in bed, when about 3 a.m. I got a call from a woman who said aliens were on her property. She said she called the police, but they didn't have anyone available to respond and she was afraid and wanted help. They told her to call me. After receiving her plea for help, I called Eric, and a half hour later we were on our way to the east end of the reservation. The caller lived about twenty miles outside of town. Eric hit the emergency light and we sped down the highway to her home. We were expecting it to be the usual sighting of illegal immigrants from Mexico or Central America. Their cartels had been operating both on and off the reservation, and the residents were very frightened by them."

"Did you see anything unusual once you arrived?" I asked.

"The closer we got to her address, the stranger the skies appeared. We saw flashing lights, balls of lights, and an occasional jagged light that emitted from a cloud-like lightning. There wasn't a storm gathering. It was such a strange atmosphere."

"How close to her house were these events occurring?"

"I'd say maybe two miles." Annie looked at Eric and he nodded.

"When you pulled in the driveway, what did you see?"

"Nothing. The house was dark. We checked our handguns, grabbed our flashlights, and walked toward the house, calling out to the female caller. We got no response."

"What did you decide to do?"

"We decided to check out the premises. I went to the left, Eric the right, and we covered the perimeter of the house. With every step, we were calling out to the occupant. As we came around the backside of the house, we saw the outline of two giant figures standing no more than twenty feet from the back of the house. Beyond them was a lighted area. As my eyes adjusted to the strange light, I made out a circular craft perched on the cliff about fifty yards from the house."

"Eric, what was your impression of what you were seeing?'

"I saw exactly what Annie is describing," he said. "I whispered to her to back away, but before we could move, two creatures came forward and took us by the arm and marched us toward the spacecraft."

"So by this time, you know you are seeing a spaceship?"

"Absolutely. There was no question," Eric said. "I have to admit, I was scared to death, but I told Annie just to stay calm, and we'd get out of this someway, somehow. I just didn't know how."

"Annie, what were you thinking at this time?" I asked.

"I was on the verge of passing out. The impact of what I was witnessing was too much for me to process. I'd never believed in UFOs. Oh, I'd heard the legends of the Star People, but to me they were just stories. I'd even watched alien movies but never in my wildest dreams did I believe I would ever encounter beings from another world."

"What happened to you once they took you onboard the craft?" I asked.

"We were taken to a room where there were about a dozen others," Eric said. "I recognized three of them as guys I knew growing up."

"Me, too," said Annie. "I saw one girl from high school and another who came back and forth to the reservation to visit relatives. The others I didn't know, but this is a big reservation and they could have been from here. I walked up to Cheyenne, the girl

I graduated with, and tried to talk to her, but she just stared right through me. I think she was hypnotized."

"Same with me. I tried talking with the guys I knew, and they didn't even acknowledge my existence."

"Everyone seemed hypnotized," said Annie, "and I was ready to freak out, when Eric suggested that we should pretend to be hypnotized, too."

"Did you do that?" I asked.

"Yes," Annie said. "At the same time, I was watching to see what was going on and trying to keep my emotions in check."

"Were you able to deceive your abductors?"

"Yes," said Eric. "If there's one thing Indians are good at is being patient. I just pretended I was waiting to see a doctor at the clinic. You know how it takes hours to see anyone. Patience is our first lesson in life." Eric laughed. "A good example of socialized medicine," he said.

"Did you ever get a good look at your abductors?" I asked.

"It was difficult," Annie said. "The rooms weren't well lit. It was difficult to make out features. They wore strange goggles that appeared to have built-in computers over their eyes. Sometimes I heard them computing."

"What do you mean by that?"

"You know, like their goggles processed data. They emitted a sound or something."

"Can you describe it?" I asked.

"No. You have to know the sound. I'd heard it before in college computer room designated for data processing."

"How tall were the creatures who took you?"

"There were those who took us onboard," said Eric, "they were giants, maybe eight feet tall. I called them the soldiers. There were small ones with the big eyes, maybe four feet tall. They did the examinations. And we saw some tall ones that were more human, but they didn't interact with us. I think they were the bosses. I kept wondering if they all lived on one planet, and if so, how did they get along?"

"Did they examine you?"

"They took blood, skin, fingernails, and hair samples," Annie said. "They attached a machine to our brain."

"How did they do that?"

"Maybe I shouldn't say brain," Annie said, "but they put on a padded cap, like a skull cap that scuba divers wear, and it had wires attached to it. When they turned it on, I kept thinking they were going to kill me. I felt a strange sensation rock my whole body like I was electrified. I kept thinking about Eric and remembering the first day we met at training camp."

"Why did you do that?"

"Before they took me, Eric told me to think of him if I got scared. So I thought of him. At first, only one of the little big-eyed creatures was looking at me, and then four more came and surrounded me. I heard them making some sounds among themselves. They kept looking at me as though they didn't understand what was going on. I just focused on Eric. Then one of them turned to the soldier. The soldier took me out of the machine. One of the small beings looked at me, and I understood my mind was worthless to them."

"The same thing happened to me," Eric said, "and they released me, too. I think that our focusing on each other didn't allow them to make our brains malleable for whatever purpose they chose. Instead, we confused them and their machines, and they let us go. The next thing we knew, we were back outside the farmhouse. We watched the spacecraft ascend and disappear. Then we saw a woman walking toward us. She was our caller. She apologized for calling. She said she got frightened when she saw strange figures but now believed it was her imagination at work."

"Do you think they manipulated her mind?"

"I think it was quite evident," said Annie. "She was definitely one of the people I saw in the UFO holding room."

"Did you tell her you saw a UFO?" Both of them shook their head.

"On our way back to headquarters," said Annie, "we decided

not to file a report. Our encounter would be our experience alone, but then we got to thinking about it. What if our strategy of thinking about something or someone else would interfere with their machines so that they cannot steal our minds?"

"Do you think that is what they were doing?"

"I definitely do. They were stealing our minds, our memories, and our souls. That was the only explanation. I think that's why we see so many people wandering the planet with no conscious or moral compass. They have lost their souls."

"When I was a boy," Eric said, "my grandfather used to tell me the ancient legends about the Shadow Stealers. They were creatures who tricked you only to take your memories and your soul. They haven't been seen for a long time. Perhaps these star travelers are the Shadow Stealers, and they have returned."

"Tell me more about the Shadow Stealers," I said.

"They were creatures that sucked out the souls of people," Eric explained. "They were often associated with caverns. Mysterious lights always announced their arrival. When people saw the lights, they hid. If you got caught out unaware, the Shadow Stealers took your memories and your soul, and you would wander around without any moral compass. It was a sad state, and families would keep a constant vigil on those who lost their souls. I think those creatures intended to steal our souls."

"Now that you two have had an encounter firsthand, what impact has it had on you?"

"For me," Annie said, "I guess I now know that life exists beyond the Earth and that's important. I don't need a government telling me otherwise. Besides, I still have bruises from where those giant soldier aliens grabbed me by the neck. She turned and showed me her four purplish bruises in the shape of fingerprints minus a thumb."

"Did the soldiers only have four digits for hands?" I asked.

"I don't know," she answered. "When they stood in the room, their hands were behind their backs like they were standing at attention like you see military men stand."

"What about you, Eric," I asked. "Do you have any bruises?"

"No bruises. I think Annie struggled too much, and they squeezed her neck harder."

"I worry the bruises will never go away. After all, it's been months and they haven't faded."

"Have you had any kind of illness related to it?" I asked.

"No. I went to the hospital, and the nurse there told me they looked like hickies to her. I never did get to see a doctor."

I knew she was referring to the infamous love bite, which is a bruise generally found on the neck, caused by a partner from hard kissing, biting, or sucking. It is most often found on teenagers.

"Do they hurt?" I asked.

"No, they don't hurt, but they're just ugly and I can't put my hair up without wearing a scarf if I wear some dresses. People will see them. God forbid they think they're hickies. I can still hear that nurse laughing."

Eric looked at her, squeezed her hand, and smiled.

"Eric, how has this encounter impacted your life?" I asked.

"For me, I'll never take a cry for help from someone reporting aliens unless I ask first if they are illegal aliens of the human kind or those from another world," Eric said smiling. "And I definitely will warn the elders that the Shadow Stealers have returned."

I see Annie and Eric occasionally. They are still working for the Homeland Security Team, although Annie has been promoted to management. Eric remains in the field and misses his partner. Lately I heard rumors of an impending wedding and am waiting for an invitation.

5. MAONE'S STORY: OUR HOPE LIES IN THE OLD WAYS

One of my former students, who was the head basketball coach at a reservation high school, requested that I stay over on a Friday night and attend one of his games. Little did I know that I had been invited to the game because it was "Appreciation Night." In other words, at half-time, the student athletes and coaches recognized the most influential person in their lives outside their family. When it came time for the head coach to announce his choice, he called my name. As I listened to the introduction and the way I had influenced his life, I was surprised when he added that I was also known as the UFO Lady in familiar circles, and if anyone had a story, they should contact me. After the honoring, I made my way to the top bleacher carrying several gifts bestowed upon me by his family. Maone approached me, introduced himself, and offered to help. When I sat down, he deposited the blankets, moccasins, and jewelry on the bleacher in front of me, and told me he had a story to tell. I visited him at his family ranch the next day.

Maone came from a very traditional family who practiced the old ways, including adhering to the Native culture, speaking the Native language in their home, and practicing the Native religion. He belonged to the wolf clan of his tribe, thus the name Maone, meaning Red Wolf in English. Built like a brick wall from the waist up, he sported a gold belt buckle indicating he was a champion bull rider. Although he stood no more than five feet eight, he was a giant of a man who reveled in his ability to teach the younger generation about their ancestral history.

"I've heard about your work with at-risk youth," I said as we walked toward the shade of a huge willow tree on his family's ranch. "It is a good thing you are doing."

"Before I begin, I want to make one thing very clear. There is a difference between the Star People of my grandfather's day and the star visitors I have met. That being said, please bear with me."

"Thank you for that clarification," I said.

"I believe kids need to know where they come from. Without that, you don't know where you're going or where you been."

I watched as he placed a horse blanket on the ground and invited me to sit. He was a gentle man who spoke softly, often hesitating as though choosing his words thoughtfully.

"You told me you had a story to tell. Would you mind if I taped it?"

"Not at all," he said. "Everyone should know the truth about the star visitors."

"When did you have your first encounter?" I asked.

"I've had them over the years since I was a teenager. I've been exposed to many things, far too advanced for a man like me. I'm nobody, but the star visitors have shared many things. I think it's because of my traditional upbringing. I believe they would like to change my resolve, to break me, in other words, or make me submit."

"Can you tell me one thing that stands out in your mind that they have used?"

"I have witnessed the most advanced technology that is possible to imagine. I have seen them use technology to interface with the mind and body and the results of their experimentation. It's beyond the scope of what humans can imagine. I've seen them take the human body and make it half machine and half human, and then control it to the point that the person will do anything they want them to do."

"I don't understand."

"The star visitors use mind control and energy harvesting to control those humans they abduct. From my perspective, it has extreme spiritual implications. They are not spiritual beings, and they show their power by destroying spirituality. Whether you're spiritual or not, you have to believe in something. I believe in the Great Mystery, God, the Great Spirit. I will not be intimidated to give up my religion, nor erase my belief in a future life. I hold fast to my beliefs. The star visitors have no beliefs; therefore, no consciousness."

"Why do you say they have no beliefs?"

"In their world, they have erased emotions and individuality. They are all alike and respond as one. They no longer speak orally. They read each other minds and have no free will."

"You said they practice mind control. Could you elaborate?" I asked.

"As I said, they control their population through mind control. Everyone thinks the same."

"So what is energy harvesting?"

"They abduct people to harvest their energy. All of us have this power within ourselves to control everything around us, and yet humans have not used that energy for centuries, and when they do, it is often misguided. The star visitors have machines that capture this energy and basically turn humans into mindless persons who will fall for anything. They can make a person forget all the teachings of their parents and grandparents and follow a leader with some bizarre notion of what is right and wrong. It is the basis of radicalism. Throwing away the old and instituting a new way even though it is not what we have been raised to believe."

"Are you saying through the energy harvesting they change people to be someone they were not raised to be?" I asked.

"Yes. Once they have completed the energy harvesting, those individuals are subject to manipulation that cause them to act in ways that would shock humanity. Riots, serial killings, torture, human trafficking. These events have become common around the world. We are losing our humanity. And it is the aliens who have brought that upon us with the assistance of power hungry individuals who work in consort with them."

"Do you mean politicians, government employees?" I asked.

"Some are politicians. Many are the extremely wealthy in society.

They've given their souls to gain their wealth. They cooperate with the enemy."

"But what about someone like you?"

"They've not touched me. I have a strong resolve of who I am. I know where I come from, who I am, and where I belong. That is why I teach the young. It is the only way to protect them. Even if they capture you and try to perform their ungodly experiments, they can't change a person who has a strong sense of person and individuality."

"Can you describe the star visitors?"

"They are like lizards. Their faces are long with a snout like a lizard or a snake. They have a long tongue that can lash out like a lizard. I have seen them eject some kind of venom from their snouts to paralyze and kill an enemy. They are frightening creatures. They terrorize those they kidnap. I'm one of the lucky ones. They found my resolve to be something they rarely encountered."

"So what do you think they want?"

"I think they plan to one day control the Earth. They already are doing it just a little at a time. We are not alone in the universe, and there are forces at work that we do not understand or can even begin to comprehend. I believe the government knows about them, but they have lied to the people so long, they can't find a way to tell the truth."

"Do you think the government will ever tell the truth?"

"If and when the truth is revealed, it will change the way we view ourselves both religiously and psychically. Humans will undergo such a transformation that we will no longer be human again. Not the human that you and I know."

"With that in mind, what do you think of this technological age, the space age, so to speak?"

"I think it's good and bad. I use the internet to follow the news of indigenous tribes in all of the Americas. What happens in South America or Canada affects all of us Indians. We are all facing the same enemy."

"Do you use email or twitter?"

"No social media but an occasional email."

"Have you shared your stories about UFOs with anyone?"

"No, only you. I think the truth of what is going on would be too difficult for most people to understand. I think they would regard me as some crazy Indian, but I'm not."

"But why tell me?"

"As Indians, we need to guard who we are. We teach our children the Red Way. It is our only hope. Your books reach more people than I can hope to reach and maybe some will take my words to heart."

I have only seen Maone once since our meeting. The number of students who are learning the old traditions doubled during that time. He is a true believer that the old ways will keep our people alive for many generations to come. I think he is right.

6. TENNESY'S STORY: THE SOUL TAKERS

Tennesy contacted me through email and asked to meet with me if I ever took a trip back East. I took him up on his invitation when I went to a family reunion. We agreed to meet at a truck stop off the interstate. When I arrived, he recognized me from my photograph and welcomed me to a back booth in the large restaurant. Tennesy, whose name in the Tsalagi (Cherokee) language means mighty warrior, appeared to be exactly that. After we ordered lunch, Tennesy wasted no time in telling me his story.

"The aliens I met were more like reptiles than humans, although there were some human qualities," he began.

"Perhaps it would be best to tell me how you came to meet the reptile people," I said.

"Sure." He paused and took a drink of his coffee. "I get excited and forget that you do not know the circumstances of my encounter."

"Please, just start at the beginning. By the way, I hope you don't mind if I tape your story."

"I don't mind." He watched as I positioned the tape recorder in the middle of the table. "I live in the mountains, not too far from here. I love the mountains. As a boy, I walked every inch of the hills behind my home with my dad, who was Cherokee. He knew the mountains like the back of his hand. He knew the herbs for healing, the plants that come in the spring that you can eat, and those that provide food and healing in the fall. He was my teacher. Now I roam the mountains alone and collect those items. My dad passed last year, but I know he still walks with me."

"I'm sorry to hear about your dad, but it appears you have many fond memories of him."

He nodded.

"So was it in the mountains behind your house where you encountered the Star People?" I asked.

"If you want to call the Reptile Men Star People, then yes. I don't regard them as the Star People of our elders. They are a different race; not human-like." He paused and looked off toward the distant mountain range. "There is a canyon that runs in the back of our house. The gorge is very deep and difficult to maintain a footing. I have only been down to the bottom of the valley once on my own power."

"Your own power?"

"By walking. It's difficult to climb back out of the canyon. Even though I'm in pretty good shape, it's a challenge."

I looked at the man who sat across from me. His muscular frame and his rough hands suggested a man who worked hard for a living. His black hair, which was parted in the middle, fell to his shoulders and outlined his strong, chiseled, bronzed face. From our emails, I knew he was a construction worker.

"So if you have only been to the canyon once on your own power, have you been to the canyon by other means?" I asked.

"Many times. The area is a heavily forested region. The valley is closed to the public, and special permits are required to enter because of the danger. For years, my people have heard unusual sounds coming from underground. There are legends about it in the area. But there is one area where glowing lights have been seen. The only way to reach it is by foot, but few have ever attempted it."

"Did you?"

He smiled, finished his cup of coffee, and signaled the waitress to bring more. "Yes. That's where I met the Reptile Men. I decided to investigate the glowing lights I'd seen the night before. I wanted to find out for myself what was going on. I was thirteen at the time." He paused and took a bite of his sandwich. "When I got to the bottom of the gorge, I discovered a long, silver, pencil-shaped craft sitting at the opening to a waterfall. Behind the waterfall was a concealed cave. Once I spotted the craft, I cautiously approached it."

"Were there any signs of life?"

"Not at first. Once I got near enough to the craft to touch it, I reached out my hand and the craft disappeared before my eyes."

"What do you mean by disappeared?"

"Just as I said. One minute I touched it, and the next minute it vanished. That's when I saw the large reptiles. I can't tell you how scared I was, and I even at thirteen I didn't scare easily. I tried to speak, but nothing came out of my mouth. I tried to move backward, but my legs wouldn't move and then the most scary thing of all happened: I was paralyzed like a stone statue. I couldn't move, and then they got inside my head."

"What do you mean they got inside your head?"

"I could hear them communicating in my head, but I didn't understand. Finally, one of them, I think he was the leader, came forth and spoke to me in Cherokee. He said I should not fear them. They were here from another world and had stopped to refuel and maintain their craft. He told me I would not remember seeing them, but that if I were interested, they would show me many wondrous things."

"Did they?"

"Over a period of three years, they showed me many things."

"Before you tell me those things, can you describe the beings to me?"

"They stood about eight feet tall. Their faces were a cross between a snake and a lizard. They had a snout for a nose. They wore vests with an insignia of a snake in yellow. No other clothing. They all seemed to be the same sex, although there were no visible sex organs. They had huge muscular arms with six-digit claws for hands. Their legs were equally muscular. They had a funny way of moving forward and backward using a rather short, powerful, thrusting motion that seemed to propel them backwards and forwards."

"How did they speak to you?"

"Like I said, they got inside my head. They took me inside the cave. It was like a big cathedral with huge stalagmites and inside this huge cathedral sat the craft I touched outside. They told me the cave was a tunnel to the universe and allowed them to travel to many worlds."

"Did they explain what they meant by traveling to other worlds?"

"They didn't have to tell me. My grandfather used to talk about a tunnel that allowed the elders to travel to other worlds and contact various races in the universe. These privileges were only for the seers or the elders, but they regularly made contact in the old days before time began."

"Did they take you into the tunnel?"

"Yes. Several times over the next three years."

"Can you tell me about your experiences?"

"They took me to other worlds and showed me advanced races and cultures. I saw the Reptile Men interact with humanoid and non-humanoid creatures. Everywhere we went, it seemed the Reptile Men were the masters, and the other creatures were subservient to them. Other beings appeared afraid and anxious in their presence, but I observed their interactions from a human perspective and that might not be what was going on at all. But yet, I feared them. I don't believe they are on Earth for any humanitarian mission."

"Why do you say that?"

"I've seen them torture humans and non-humans. I've seen them steal their souls."

"How do they steal their souls?"

"They have machines that take your soul. At least I think that's what they do. Once a person or creature is put into the machine, they follow orders blindly. They have no will of their own. It worries me."

"Were you ever put into the machine?"

He nodded.

"But it didn't work on me."

"Do you know why?"

He shook his head. "All I know is they kept trying, but it only increased my resolve to not allow them to take my soul."

"How did you manage that?"

"You are probably going to think this strange. I recited an ancient prayer my grandfather taught me when they put me in the machine. My Pops taught me this prayer as a means to overcome fear. Over and over again, I recited the prayer. The machine didn't work. I think the words of my grandfather were too powerful for them. I think that is the key. They have no spirituality. But humans by nature are spiritual. At least those of us who know the old ways."

"Do you think other prayers would have the same effect?" I asked.

"I don't know. I never tried it. I stayed with what I knew the best. My grandfather's prayer is powerful. It comes from the ancients in the time before time. He learned it from his grandfather, who learned it from his grandfather. It has been passed down through the ages of time. I will stick with it. It's what I know."

"Can you tell me why you contacted me?" I asked.

"I wanted you to tell my story because I believe the Reptile Men have plans for Earth. I think they want to make humans subservient to them. If you write my story, tell the people that if they are taken, to pray their own prayer to prevent the Reptile Men from capturing their soul. Perhaps if everyone did this, we will discourage them. This is why I tell you my story. It's maybe the most important thing I will ever do."

"Do the Reptile Men still visit you?"

"They gave up after I joined the Army to try to get away from them. But I know they are out there kidnapping others and performing their soul-taking project. They must be stopped. Just tell everyone to remember to recite their most powerful prayer if they are ever taken."

I keep in touch with Tennesy by email. He still works in construction although he has a master's degree in business administration. When he wants to talk about the "soul takers," he calls me on a TracFone for fear the government might locate him. He recently became engaged and plans to marry next spring. I promised to attend his wedding. To date, the Reptile Men have not returned.

7. RAMBO'S STORY: AN INTERRUPTED FISHING TRIP

Rambo planned his weekend fishing trip down to the last detail. He packed his motorcycle bags the night before his trip. He planned to leave the next morning at dawn. At around 5:00 a.m., he saw a star moving across the sky. He disregarded it and continued on his journey to his favorite fishing campsite. In hindsight, he often thought that had he paid more attention, he would not have become a victim of the ungodly creatures that interrupted his weekend.

I met Rambo at his mother's house. When I arrived, there were a dozen or more children playing in the front yard. Rambo appeared in the doorway and yelled at the children to go play. Before entering the house, I handed a bag of cookies to the oldest girl. "They're my sisters' kids," Rambo explained. "They went shopping today and dropped off the kids. They can be a rowdy bunch."

I followed Rambo into the kitchen and sat down at the dining table. "Your mother invited me to meet you. She told me you had an encounter a few months ago, and I've come to hear your story." I watched the young twenty something as he looked in the refrigerator. He could have been a poster boy for a heavy metal rock group of the '80s with long flowing hair that fell to the middle of his back. He frequently stopped and pushed his hair behind his ears revealing studded earrings. He wore jeans, cowboy boots, and a black t-shirt with a white buffalo skull. Black studded, leather cuffs wrapped around his wrists, and a large, turquoise crucifix hung on a silver chain around his neck. Tattoos of famous Indian warriors covered every part of his visible body except his face.

"What's your pleasure," he said. "We got Coke, 7 Up, and coffee." When he returned to the table with two cups of black coffee, he relaxed and smiled the most engaging smile I had seen in a long time.

"Your mother told me that you had an encounter a few months ago when you set out on a fishing trip. Would you be willing to tell me about it?" I asked.

"How much did she tell you?" he asked.

"Only that you had had an encounter and that you were having nightmares about it."

"Don't tell anyone about the nightmares," he laughed. "It might soil my macho image."

"Your image is safe with me," I said as I placed the tape recorder on the table. "Maybe you could start by telling me about yourself."

"My name is John, but I everyone calls me Rambo." He paused and flexed his bulging muscles. Whether he had any other similarities to the Rambo of the movies was not yet apparent.

"Can you tell me what happened that morning when you set out on your fishing trip?" I asked.

"I set out just as a streak of light could be seen on the horizon. I was traveling east. In the distant sky, I saw a star moving across the sky. I thought it was a satellite at first. Then I saw it getting larger as it moved in a southerly direction. I thought no more of it, because I was taking a left hand turn at about that time heading north to my destination. I kick myself when I think about it. If I had paid more attention, I might have outrun them or, at the least, hidden from them."

"How long did you travel before you saw the UFO again?" I asked.

"The next time I saw it, it looked like the moon. It was a huge ball of light. As I gazed at it in disbelief, I saw four smaller spheres come out of the ball of light—one was headed directly at me. Realizing my situation, I kick started my motorcycle and headed off-road to the cover of some trees that ran along the river. Under the cover of the trees, I saw an object hovering over the river that was about forty-feet wide."

"What was the craft doing?"

"At first I thought it was just skimming the river. Then, I saw a whirlwind created in my fishing spot, and it was like a tornado sucking up the water from the river. I saw two beings, which looked like large lizards, jump into the water once the suction ended. They were bathing or swimming. I'm not sure."

"Can you describe them?"

"They looked like big lizards and yet they walked like men. They had huge legs and arms and barrel chests. I remember thinking I would not want to get in a fight with them. One swipe from one of their hands would knock me unconscious."

"What about their faces?" I asked.

"Their heads were rounded in the back, reminding me of pictures I'd seen of big monkeys on the NatGeo channel. Their foreheads were high up, but the rest of their faces were flat. Their noses were flat and their mouths were huge. They didn't seem to have ears, but I knew they could hear. When I stepped on a twig, they both turned in my direction. At the same time, the craft began to move upward in my direction. I tried to start my motorcycle, but it wouldn't turn over. I got off and started running. When the craft was over me, I felt its power. I was unable to move."

"What did the two alien creatures do?" I asked.

"They came up to me. One stood on my right side and the other on my left side, and we began moving upward toward the craft."

"How did you feel?"

"For some strange reason, the fear I felt was gone."

"Did they attempt to communicate with you?"

"Not while we're going into the craft."

"What happened when you entered the spaceship?"

"I was in a large domed room. The feeling had returned to my body. I could walk around, but the two huge creatures stood by the entrance. I knew they were not going to let me go, and then the door opened and another one, identical to the two, walked into the room."

"What did the third one do?" I asked.

"He approached me and told me through my mind that I had nothing to fear. He also let me know it was useless to resist. The next thing I remember was being placed in a horizontal position on a table that was not there before. When I entered the room there was nothing there, but suddenly a table is there. I looked up into the eyes of this creature, and I felt a stabbing pain in my neck. I had a feeling of being carried to another place on the ship. I didn't struggle, but I had no power to struggle anyway."

He paused, drained his coffee cup, walked to the counter, and poured another cup. He looked out the window and pointed to his mother. I got up and looked out the window. She had a basket full of fresh tomatoes.

"Did you lose consciousness?" I asked.

"For part of the time. I came to a strange room that was probably a laboratory. I was not familiar with the equipment, but then they were aliens. Besides, I had limited knowledge of labs. We had one in a chemistry lab in college, but I dropped the class and had little experience in it."

"What were they doing in the lab?"

"I felt a strange burning in my arm. I looked at it and realized they were taking my blood. I tried to get up, but I couldn't move. I yelled at them but they paid no attention. I gave up and lay there quietly, and at some point I passed out again."

"Do you know how long you were on the craft?" I asked.

"About four hours."

"How did you get off the craft?"

"I don't know. My next memory was sitting under a tree by the river. I knew by the movement of the sun it was the around noon. I tried to stand, but I was too weak. I crawled over to my bike, opened the saddlebags, and pulled out a bottle of Gatorade. I drank the whole thing. I threw up violently. After some time passed, I got another bottle and drank it too. This one I kept down. After that, I fell asleep. I woke up in the late afternoon and was able to stand even though I was wobbly. I managed to get on my bike, and it started up immediately."

"Hello," Molly said as she walked into the kitchen. "I see you've met my son. He's a good boy. He works and supports us. Not too many twenty-six-year olds around here would take on that job." I watched Rambo's reaction, and he appeared embarrassed but at the same time proud.

"What kind of work do you do?" I asked Rambo.

"I'm a computer technician for the tribe," he said.

"He's too modest," said Molly. "He runs the whole system for the tribe. The telephone system, all the tribal government internet systems, and the schools. Without him, the tribe would still be in the dark ages." Rambo smiled as his mother went to the sink and washed the tomatoes and drained them on paper towels.

"Did you continue with your fishing trip?" I asked him.

"No. Once I got my motorcycle started, I came home. The house was empty. I was nauseous and had a severe pain in my stomach that wouldn't go away. Mom was not here. I crawled in bed and slept for fourteen hours."

"Molly tells me you suffer from nightmares," I said.

"The nightmares started shortly after the abduction. I'm always on the ship, and they're experimenting on my body. I see them open my stomach and remove my insides and examine them and reattach them. They seem to be communicating with one another. I wake up covered with a cold sweat."

"Why do you think you are having such dreams?" I asked.

"It scared me to death the first time it happened," his mother interrupted. "I heard him cry out. I ran into his bedroom, and he was sitting in the bed holding his stomach. I shook him and he finally woke up. I was frightened and he was frightened. I went into the kitchen, made hot chocolate, and we sat up the rest of the night talking about his nightmares and his abduction." She walked over to Rambo's side and patted him on the shoulder.

"But it happened again," Rambo said. "The same dream repeatedly. It never stops. I close my eyes and the creatures are there. I can't forget them."

"Well, show her," Molly demanded. He stood and walked toward me. He pulled up his t-shirt. Down the center of his hairless, washboard stomach was a thin white line. "Does that look like a scar to you?" she asked.

There was no question. It was a scar.

"I believe they operated on me and took out my insides," Rambo said, "and in my dreams I relive it. I just want it to stop."

"Do your nightmares occur every night?" I asked.

He nodded.

"I wonder if you will spend the night," Molly said to me in a pleading voice, "and when it happens, perhaps you can talk with Johnny. I know he can overcome this. I just want you to witness it and try to help him make sense of it. It's ruining his life."

After lunch, Rambo invited me to join the family in a game of softball. Even the youngest, who was probably five, participated. Afterwards, hot and exhausted, we found comfort under the shade of a tree while the children took turns diving into a play pool.

"Do you think there is hope for me?" Rambo asked, as we watched the children show off their skills.

"I think the mind has a remarkable way of healing itself. It might take time, but the first thing you have to do is accept what happened to you. Claim it as your own and accept the fact that you were abducted by beings far more intelligent than you and me, and that they performed experiments on you."

"But they were lizard men. How do I accept that?"

"That's possibly the first step in healing," I said. "We are the dominant species on this planet Earth, but who knows what kind of species exist on other worlds. They may have had millions of years to adapt and develop. I accept the fact that the visitors, whatever shape they may be, are smarter than me if they can travel through space and visit us."

"Doesn't it bother you that they are lizards?"

"No. You are not the first person to encounter them. You will not be the last, but perhaps telling your story will help others."

"But they have changed my life forever. I don't go fishing any more. I stay around the house. How many twenty-six-year olds do you know who stay around the house with his mom?" he asked.

"To be honest, I know quite a few. But don't change your routine. Go on your fishing trips. It is likely the lizard men will not return. Few people have told me about repeated abductions by lizard men. If you don't want to go alone, take a friend. Take that first step toward healing."

"Well, that's comforting." He laughed and called out to his nephew who was teasing one of his younger siblings.

I stayed the night with Molly and Johnny Rambo. Along toward midnight Rambo entered the living room where Molly and I were watching a rerun of the old film *The Night of the Living Dead*. He sat down between us and took both of our hands.

"I didn't wake up because of the nightmare," he explained. "I woke up because I had to go to the bathroom."

The three of us laughed and watched the main character in the movie, who was hiding in the closet to escape the zombies but was killed at the end by government men.

"So much for surviving a zombie attack," Molly said as she turned off the tv.

"Or a lizard abduction," added Rambo. We laughed and headed off to bed. The rest of the evening was uneventful. Molly was convinced that talking about his ordeal had healed her son. I was more skeptical.

The next morning, I asked Rambo to take me fishing. At first, he was reluctant, but with the encouragement of his mom and me, he relented. By 9 a.m., Molly had packed sandwiches and cold drinks, and we set off on his motorcycle. As we came upon the spot of his abduction, we sat in the shade of a huge willow tree and he relived those fateful moments once again. As the day passed, he relaxed, and before we headed home, we both had caught our limit. We rode home in silence.

When we reached the porch, Rambo turned toward me and said, "I know what you did today. You made me face my demons.

Thanks." He smiled and then said, "Are you going to help me clean these fish?"

For the next three months, I talked with Rambo every night at midnight regardless of where I was. On several occasions, he woke with the same nightmare, but as time passed the nightmares were less frequent. He took my advice and instead of fighting them, he wrote about them in a diary. He is now being honored by the tribe for the role he played in bringing the tribe into the 21st century. He has invited me to attend the ceremony. I plan to be there.

8. WILEY'S STORY: LOST TIME AMONG THREE ALIEN SPECIES

Wiley was a thirty-four-year-old American Indian doctor who went on a solo hunting trip. Although he remembered his abduction, he had no idea that he had been missing for three days. It was not until he returned to town three days late and confronted a search party that he discovered his missing time. This is the story of his encounter.

I met Wiley at the entrance to the Indian Health Hospital. We walked around the back of the institution and sat on a bench under a huge aspen tree.

"I work nights at the hospital in the ER," Wiley began. "It's a stressful job and one with little rewards. If someone comes into the ER, it's usually a serious case and often ends in death. There are times I see the same person three or four times a week, mostly drug overdose or alcohol poisoning. Sometimes I need to get away from it all and away from people. That's when I go hunting or camping. That's where I had my encounter."

He paused and stood looking off toward the emergency entrance. He was a small man with a slight build. If he had any muscles, they were well hidden under the lab coat and denim jeans. I noticed a slight limp as he moved about the kitchen, but I tried unsuccessfully not to notice his movement.

"I was born with a birth defect," Wiley explained. "Doctors told my mom I would never walk, but she found a doctor who believed he could help me. The two of them never gave up, and after twenty-six surgeries, at the age of nine, I took my first steps. I was so impressed by the hospital staff and my doctor that I knew I wanted to be a doctor."

"Please tell me about your hunting trip where you had your encounter," I said.

"Every year since I've been here, I go hunting. I enjoy getting out away from everything. I always go alone, which may not be the smartest thing to do, but it's the way I keep my sanity from all the pain I see every day. My adopted Mom—I'm not from this reservation so she's my mom while I'm here—loves deer meat. I rent a room from her. Although I have kitchen privileges, she cooks a big lunch before I go to work and packages up leftovers for the evening. The arrangement works for both of us. I bring the deer; she cooks for me."

"Where do you go hunting?"

"Here, on the reservation. I've been here four years, so I know the area fairly well. My dad taught me about the woods. I can find my way home so I don't worry about getting lost."

"Can you tell me about your abduction?"

"It happened on my second night in camp. I had just turned in for the night. Everything was dark, and just as I was about to fall asleep, bright lights lit up the campsite. Lights so bright that you would've thought you were on the strip in Las Vegas. I scrambled out of my tent to find the source of the light, but I was blinded by its intensity. Shielding my eyes, I watched as a huge craft quietly set down in the meadow where I was camped. It was no more than thirty yards from my campsite."

"What are you thinking at this point?" I asked.

"Fear at first. My first thoughts were to run, but it was dark and I decided that was a foolish idea. So I settled down and decided to watch. It was not long until several beings descended from the craft. I wanted to greet them, but I knew that was just as foolish as running away. So I remained hidden as I watched the entities walk around the outside of the craft. It was not long until they began to spread out and walk in various directions; one was walking directly toward me. When it was no more than ten feet from me, I stood and it stopped. I knew it was measuring me up and down. It had an advantage because all I saw was a darkened silhouette against the lights of the craft, so I couldn't make out any features. After a few seconds, the entity gave off a shrill call and two huge beings came to its side. It pointed and the large beings came forth and grabbed me by my arms."

"Did you react in any way?"

"I tried to speak, but I was unable to utter a word. I shined my flashlight in its face, and that's when I realized the small entity was a female. I didn't get a chance to look at the larger creatures before they grabbed me."

"When you shined the flashlight in her direction, did you get a look at her?" I asked.

"The being was about my size, about five-feet-six-inches tall. She wore a helmet and a light-colored suit—like silver or light blue or gray. There was light colored hair falling from beneath her helmet. Suddenly I found myself on board the craft. Once inside, I didn't see the female, only the creatures who stood beside me and some smaller creatures with big helmets."

"Can you describe those creatures?"

"The best thing I can say is they were like huge lizards, yet they walked upright like a man. Their skin was shiny and slick except for their heads, which were bulky. They were brown and green. A huge stubby tail rested on the floor. They had huge mouths like lizards that wrapped around the sides of their faces. The smaller ones conducted the experiments, not the lizards."

"Can you describe the craft?"

"I was dumfounded by the size. I was inside an entry that appeared as big as a football field. There were huge tanks in the center of the area—as large as a city's water holding tanks, but transparent. There were six of them, and there was some kind of liquid inside that moved up and down almost like a lava lamp. At first, I thought it was water storage, but water is not that heavy. I walked toward them but was pulled in another direction by one of the beings. I asked what they were; I understood they had something to do with the atmosphere, but nothing more. I asked for more information, but there was no explanation."

"How long did you remain in this area?"

"Not long enough. There were other mysterious machines in this area, mostly banked against the walls. The walls were concave, and the machines were built to meld into them. They looked similar to huge computers, but when I asked about them I understood they had something to do with their guidance system. Before I could ask any more questions, I was guided out of the room and taken to another level. I entered a small room that contained three other men. Two seemed to be totally oblivious to what was going on, but the third, like me, was fully aware of where he was and, like me, had no idea of how he ended up on the craft. He told me his name was Frederick. He told me he was I doctor. I told him I was too. We agreed, if possible, to contact each other should we remember this event if we were freed."

"Have you been in contact with Frederick since the event?" I asked.

He nodded.

"How were you able to contact each other?"

"I found him on the internet."

"Have you seen him since your abduction?"

"We've talked for hours on the phone. We met last year during the New Year's holiday. Fred lives in New York City. He invited me to New York for the New Year's celebration, and I took him up on it."

"Let's go back to the abduction, do you remember what happened to you while you were onboard?" I asked.

"Both Fred and I were subjected to experiments where the abductors informed us that they were copying all of our knowledge. When I objected, they made me aware they could take the information painlessly or painfully. I knew they were serious, so I tried to resist physically, but I'm not brave at all. I tried with all my might to sabotage what they were doing, but they seemed pleased with the information they obtained."

"How did you try to sabotage them?"

"For example, I thought about diabetes and inserted lines from the poem, 'Casey at the Bat,' in my head. I know that sounds crazy, but my eight-grade English teacher forced the whole class to memorize that poem by heart, and it was the only thing that came to mind. Mrs. Crookshank, our teacher, told us that it was good to have a poem in our heads so that if we were ever frightened or felt alone, we could always recite the poem and feel better."

"How did you feel about the star travelers stealing your knowledge?"

"Madder than hell. I don't know if my attempts at sabotage worked, but I knew I was in the presence of beings who felt they were superior to humans, and yet they took the time to steal my knowledge. I hope I corrupted it. Like I said, I repeated the poem, 'Casey at the Bat' the entire time I was inside the tube. I know it sounds silly but it was the only weapon I had and, like Mrs. Crookshank said, it helped alleviate my fear."

"You mentioned being placed in a tube. Can you explain?" I asked.

"It was a tube with a machine that encircled my head. That's all I can tell you. Fred remembers the same thing. But neither of us had ever seen anything like it before."

"Did the smaller men ever remove the helmets?"

"I don't think they wore helmets. Their heads were just bigger and rounder than humans. They had very strange eyes. Although they had human form and walked upright like humans, they weren't human. I think there were three species working together on the ship."

"Can you elaborate?"

"First there was the human-like female. Then the lizard men. And the small men. I think they all worked together. The small men's eyes were large and seemed to wrap half-way around their heads. Their pupils were quite prominent and almost appeared like lenses on a camera that could retract. Their eyes seemed to change with the light. Their arms were too perfect, like they were mechanical. Sometimes, I thought I had not met real aliens, but robots. I still am not sure. Neither is Fred, although he claims he saw several humanoids in a hallway that may have been the real culprits. It was sometime after I was subjected to their knowledge-taking machine that I met the female who made first contact with me."

"How do you know she was female?"

"By the way she looked. She looked like a female. She was dainty and had a female form. She had long blond hair, which I later came to the conclusion was fake."

"Tell me about that encounter."

"After the one alien who said he was recording my knowledge had completed his task, I was taken to a room where I was alone. Shortly thereafter, a female entity entered the room. I understood she was a doctor and ordered me to disrobe. When I resisted, the door opened, and two of the lizard men entered and removed my clothes. They had claws for hands, and when I resisted they scratched the hell out of my arms. After they removed my clothes, I was attached to a table, and despite my efforts to sit up, I couldn't move. It felt like some kind of an invisible clamp had circled my wrists and ankles."

"There was nothing visible?"

"Nothing. As I started to struggle, the female moved toward me with a large suction like apparatus. She touched my body and indicated that I was a perfect human specimen. I couldn't understand that, considering my surgeries. After that, I think I blanked out because I have no further memories of that event."

"Do you have any other memories of what occurred while you were onboard the craft?"

"I have this strange memory of them forcing me to ejaculate." He paused and rubbed his eyes. "I know it sounds crazy, but when I told Fred about my memory, he said that he had the same experience, only he remembered it. I guess both of us were sperm donors for the aliens. It is bizarre, I know."

"Can you remember anything else?" I asked.

"I remember that they wanted me to go with them. The whole idea was frightening and threatening to me."

"What did you tell them?"

"I told them I had to return to Earth. I had a job and responsibilities. People depended on me and if I did not return, the authorities would search for me. That's another thing. I remember that we did not stay on Earth."

"When I first met you, you told me that you were missing three days. Can you explain that?"

"I have no explanation. When I planned the trip, it was for three days. When I returned, I had been gone six days."

"Can you tell me what happened when you were returned to Earth?" I asked.

"I woke up in my sleeping bag. I went about the rest of the week, hunting and camping. I bagged a deer and processed it for the meat plant. On Sunday, I broke camp and that's when I remembered what had happened. My brain exploded with images. I drove like a madman for town, only to discover it was not Sunday, but Wednesday. I had no explanation for why I was gone so long and that's when I realized that the aliens had detained me for three days."

"Did you tell anyone what had happened?"

"No. Once I got back to my room, I showered and sat down at my computer to search for Frederick. It took several searches before I found him. I remembered he was from New York City, I remembered he was a doctor, and I knew his first name. It took several hours, but I found him and immediately sent him an email. It was the strangest email I had ever written. I was asking a stranger if he remembered me."

"Did he?" I asked.

"I didn't have time to shut off my computer before a new mail appeared in my mailbox. It was from Fred. It said call me and gave me his cell number."

"Did he confirm your abduction?"

"That and more. He remembered a lot of details. He discovered that all four of us who were abducted, including the two in the room who resembled zombies, were in fact, doctors. So they purposely chose and abducted people from the medical field and stole their knowledge. Fred had the same experience as I. He, too, was missing three days. In fact, he had missed a flight to Paris that he had planned for months."

"Does he remember encountering a female?"

He nodded.

"He was lured on board by a female with long blond hair. Later he encountered a bald female who came into his room and examined him. We decided that her blond hair must have been a wig to make her look more human. She touched his body all over, and when he woke, he had a red circle about the size of a quarter near his navel."

"So have the two of you remained friends?"

"Yes. I mentioned that I flew to New York City for New Year's. We are meeting in Las Vegas for the next New Year's celebration. He is bringing his girlfriend, and I would like to invite you. Don't get me wrong, I know you are married, but for your research, you might like to meet him. We are still comparing notes and trying to understand why they wanted our knowledge. It would seem to me that if they are superior to humans, why would they need our knowledge? It doesn't make sense. Obviously, they are advanced if they can visit Earth and fly those enormous machines. So why would they want to know what we know? After repeated discussions and emails and soul-searching on the part of both of us, we think we know the answer." He paused and stood up. He looked at his watch. "I have to go soon," he said. "I'm the only doctor on duty tonight."

"Are you going to tell me what you think was the reason for your abduction?"

"Fred and I think they are looking for human vulnerabilities. Like what kills us. What viruses and plagues will wipe out the human race. They breathe air like we do and seem to function well within our environment. So I think they are looking for some way to wipe us out without raising a weapon or experiencing resistance. I think they have learned enough about us to know we will not go down without a fight. But we still haven't figured out how we lost three days."

"Have you considered hypnosis?"

"Not yet. We both hope all of our memories will come back."

"Is there anything else you can remember?" I asked.

"Just one thing. Remember, I said that they had claws and forcefully undressed me?"

I nodded.

He unbuttoned his shirt. On his chest were three large white scars. He buttoned his shirt and pulled up is left sleeve. Three round scars were on his upper arm. "The round scars are from a puncture wound they made by their long talons as I struggled with them. The scars on my chest were made by their claws."

"Does your friend have similar scars?" I asked.

"On his legs where they picked him up and placed him on the table. We were both victims and have the scars to prove it."

I am still in contact with Wiley. He emails occasionally and fills in some of the missing links to his abduction, but the original story has not changed. I have been invited to join Wiley and Fred in Las Vegas to bring in the New Year. My husband and I plan to join them. I hope to learn more when I meet Fred.

9. DOLI'S STORY: THEY EVOLVED DIFFERENTLY

I met Doli at a conference in Phoenix. She was accompanying her mother who was the keynote speaker at the event. As we filed into the auditorium to hear to her mother's speech, she mentioned that she had read my books. When we were seated, she leaned over and whispered that the Star People had visited her since she was eight years old. She agreed to meet me that evening to tell her story.

Doli was a statuesque young woman who stood nearly six feet tall. Her thick, straight, black hair hung midway down her back, but what stood out most of all were the flashing smile and the two distinct dimples on her cheeks.

We met at the sports bar in the conference hotel, selecting a booth that was out of the way of the main traffic. Other than an occasional appearance of our waiter, nearly all the patrons were glued to the widescreen TVs broadcasting football, volleyball, and soccer games simultaneously.

After the waiter deposited our ginger ales and a bowl of pretzels, Doli asked me: "How many people approach you about having encountered the Star People?"

"I would say that about fifty percent of the people I interview are individuals I've never met. Then another ten percent would be individuals I've known sometimes for many years before they tell me their story. About twenty percent are either friends or are relatives or acquaintances of friends who know of someone who has had an encounter. The remainder are individuals like you. Just a chance introduction, not expecting a story. I mean, I've known your mother professionally for about twenty years, but I didn't know she had a daughter. And more importantly, I didn't know you had a story to tell."

"So fate, right?" Doli asked.

I nodded. "Sometimes it's uncanny. Like someone is pulling me to that person. Or divine intervention that I meet someone like you. After my first book came out, I was contacted by many individuals who heard of my research."

"How many of those individuals have never told anyone?" she asked.

"Almost all of them. Some have told a trusting relative or an elder but were told to remain silent. I've only interviewed about five individuals who were very open about their encounters and broadcasted it to anyone who would listen."

"I fall into the former category," she said. "When I was eight, I remember being at my grandmother's. She was an old-fashioned woman who lived by the traditional beliefs. My grandmother's name was Pretty Sage Woman. She named me Doli, which means Bluebird Woman. When I was born, I had blue eyes. Grandma said the bluebird was the prettiest of all birds, and that when I became a woman, I must be the prettiest among all women of the tribe. Not the prettiest in physical appearance but the prettiest in the heart. I was to follow the old ways and be kind and humble to those who came to my door despite their station in life. So the homeless, the beggar, the unwed mother would be treated in the same manner as a king, a queen, a wealthy CEO, or a powerful leader. I take her words very seriously. I accept my fate and have tried to live up to her expectations. So when I met the Star People, I accepted them with the same kindness. It was not until I became a teenager that I realized the ramifications of the importance of my interactions with them."

"How old are you now?"

"I'm twenty-three. I'm working on my PhD in entomology."

"I'm not surprised. You have a good role model in your mother," I said.

"She was the first one to receive a PhD in our tribe. Until

mom, no one believed that an Indian could get a PhD."

"But why entomology?" I asked.

"The Star People I met are not humanoid. From my early childhood, I had a fascination with insects. I wanted books about them. I would go to the university with my mother and go to the biology department and view the insects and ask questions of anyone who would listen to me. Now, I concentrate on the aspects of molecular genetics, biomechanics, morphology, and developmental biology in the field."

"Are you telling me that the aliens you met are more like insects than human and that has spurred your interest in entomology?"

"Yes!" she replied excitedly and then looked around the room to see if anyone had noticed her enthusiasm.

"Can you go back to the time you were eight years old and tell me about your first encounter?"

"As I said, I was at my grandmother's house. Back in the late seventies, early eighties maybe, the federal government had a program to assist new homeowners. If they had five acres of land, the government would provide a loan to build a house on those acres. The owner had to contribute their land and labor to the building of the home. After that, the owners made monthly mortgage payments, but the land and their labor was the down payment. My grandmother and grandpa got one of those loans. They built a home in the country and were independent of grocery stores. My grandmother grew a garden, canned and dried food for the winter. My grandfather raised hogs and chickens and sold them for the items they needed from the store and to pay their small electric bill. To me, their life was perfect. It was during my eighth summer that I first met the Insect Men, the Star People."

"Tell me about it."

"By the time I was eight, I was independent. It was berry-picking season, and I begged my grandmother to let me go alone to the draw near the house to pick berries. She gave me her watch and told me that I could only stay for two hours, and then she would come for me if I didn't return. I remember climbing down in the draw. One of the new puppies was just as adventurous as I was, and he and I were having a grand old time. When I got to the bottom of the ravine, I saw this giant, flattened, silver ball among the shrub trees. Honey, my little puppy, began to back away and bark, but I couldn't resist going forward. I walked among the Russian thistles quietly, but the trees were scrawny and provided little cover. Suddenly I felt a hand on my shoulder, and when I turned around I came face to face with a huge insect. I don't remember being afraid. I loved insects, and the creature reminded me of a giant insect. But when he spoke to me, I was very confused."

"How did he speak to you?"

"At the time, I didn't know that I simply understood his thoughts."

"Did he abduct you?" I asked.

"No. He invited me to join him on his ship. I went willingly. He was a collector of insects, too, and he studied them. I was so fascinated, and he showed me his collection."

"Did he tell you why he was collecting insects?"

"Not at first. He simply showed me his collection, which I remember being mind-boggling. I had never seen such an array of insects."

"Did he take samples of your blood or hair?"

"No. Nothing like that. He told me that they planned to leave that night, but he would see me again."

"Did you see him again?" I asked.

"Every year since our first encounter, I have seen him. My grandmother left me her home after she passed. I still spend my holidays and summers there when I have a break from school. I go there to meet my Insect Man. He always knows when I plan to return and he comes there."

"How does he know?"

"Telepathy. We are in contact even across the vast space in the Universe."

"How does he do that?"

"I don't know. I just know it happens," she replied as she looked in the direction of a crowd of young men cheering their team's touchdown.

"Is he the only one who comes during his visits?"

"No, there are others, but he is the Chief or leader. The others do as he says."

"When he showed you his collection, were the insects alive or dead?" I asked

"The whole top level of the spaceship was devoted to his study. There were both live specimens and preserved specimens of the same insect. They even had pairs, both male and female, if appropriate, to encourage reproduction."

"Why were they studying insects?"

"Because they were the closest relative they had on Earth. He was interested in the evolution of the insects on Earth as well as paleontology as it related to entomology. He studied how insects of Earth had changed over time and the effects of the environment on the evolution of the insects."

"When you left him that day, what did you do?"

"I picked berries. But I lost track of time and came home late to a big scolding. When I told my grandmother about my encounter, she pulled me onto her lap and held me tightly. There are stories, she told me, about how the Insect People saved the lives of the people by providing them food during the Hungry Moon." I was aware that her tribe referred to the month of February as the Hungry Moon because it was usually a time of year when hunting was difficult and food supplies had dwindled.

"In the old days my tribe had a very special relationship with the Insect People and, according to Grandma, my encounter was a sacred encounter. Not very many people from the tribe have seen them. She cautioned me to keep my encounter close to my heart because too many people today are unfamiliar with the relationship of the people and the Insect people. So I never told anyone, not even my mother, about my Insect Man."

"So why are you telling me?" I asked.

"When I became a teenager, I became as obsessed with alien

abductions as I was about entomology. I used to go to the library and order books through the librarian about UFOs. I came to believe they existed. My mom knew of my obsession, but she figured it was another one of my quirky interests and I'd outgrow it. Last Christmas, as sort of a gag gift, she gave me your books."

She paused and giggled. "Sorry, I know I said a gag gift, but your books were anything but a gag. I read them twice during the holidays. I was impressed with how you treated the subject and your clients. When I heard that you were also speaking at the conference, I purposely invited myself to accompany my mom. I knew it was time to tell my story. There are not many stories about the insect men, but those that do exist are about frightening experiences. I've had just the opposite."

She paused and ordered another ginger ale when the waiter stopped by our table.

"What is your overall perspective of them?"

"That they are extremely intelligent beings, and because of their environment they evolved as the dominant species on their planet. I always find it interesting that people believe that if there were space travelers they would look like humans. While those species do exist in the universe, there are hundreds of species that have evolved differently. They do not have the environment found on Earth, so their development is different. Thus, I'm focusing on the developmental process, the biometrics of movement, the molecular genetics, and biomechanics of the insect and how it relates to the evolution of the Insect Men."

"That is a rather interesting field of study, but I certainly understand why you would choose that field given your interests and experiences. Are the Star People or Insect People aware of your study?"

"They are not only aware, but they have allowed me to research them. Of course, it is research that I cannot divulge in scientific circles for fear of being discredited, but it has been the most fascinating journey."

"Then why bother?" I asked.

"You should understand that as an academic. Someday, the people of Earth may make contact with them. If that day comes, I want to be ready to help humans understand the nature of the Insect People. I know that if this time comes, human reaction will no doubt be one of fear and hostility. Humans always try to destroy what they do not understand."

I keep in contact with Doli. She is one of the most amazing women I have ever met. While she has traveled with the Insect Men to some of the most remote locations on the planet to study insects, she cannot reveal what she has learned. Despite the fact that she travels a different path in the field of entomology, she remains a well-grounded individual who is considered brilliant among her peers and professors. More than that, she lives up to her name as being the prettiest woman of her tribe by treating others with respect. I, for one, am fortunate to call her my friend.

10. AL'S STORY: SOME MEN ARE WINDSHIELDS; SOME ARE THE BUGS

Al, short for Aloquisha, was a volunteer counselor for veterans in his home state of Alaska. A "survivor" of the U.S. Government was the way he described himself. He told me that being a survivor was part of his nature. When he was two years old, his family was uprooted from their home on the Aleutian Islands; he along with other families from nine villages were herded into military transport ships. Because the Japanese were making aggressive forays into the Aleutian Islands, the U.S. military removed all families from their homes. Stories of the U.S. military burning their homes and churches so they would not fall into Japanese hands were told and retold by family members. His father, who could not take the cramped facilities provided the families, joined the military and was awarded the Bronze Star when the U.S. invaded Attu Island. Whether he was talking about the family evacuation or Vietnam, to Al it was all the same. He was a survivor of U.S. aggression whether it was Alaska or Vietnam.

I met the Vietnam veteran at a VA Center in the middle of the state. When I told him that Ute, the veteran I met in Hawaii, had recommended I talk with him, he smiled. "How is Ute?" he asked.

"He is doing well. He has a small coffee farm on the Big Island. A wife and two beautiful daughters and four sons. He told me to tell you that the door is always open should you decided to experience paradise."

Al smiled.

"I don't ordinarily talk about Vietnam except to veterans," he said as he served up two cups of coffee from an urn that probably held a hundred cups. "But if Ute said you are okay, you must be."

I followed the seventy-two-year-old veteran to a table that looked like it belonged in a school cafeteria. He walked with a limp, which he claimed was a result of a run-in with a polar bear. His short hair was peppered with gray. A large white scar, which he attributed to the same bear, was visible at the top of his skull. The tip of his index finger on his right hand was missing. He shuffled his feet as he walked, a sign of the arthritis that riddled his body.

"How old were you when you went to Vietnam?" I asked.

"I celebrated by nineteenth birthday two days after I arrived in country. I was a boy with dreams of following in my father's footsteps. The trouble of it was, the Vietnamese were no threat to us. It was hard killing men who looked like me," he said. "After a while I questioned the whole war. Twice I was put in the brig for insubordination. That's where I met Ute. We were both rebels with a cause." He paused and smiled to himself and took a drink of his coffee.

"Did you volunteer for the army or were you drafted?"

"No, I volunteered. My dad told me it was a good thing. He felt America was under attack. But it wasn't, and they're still doing it, too. Why do you think we're in Iraq and Afghanistan? It isn't because they are a threat to us. We just want to control the world, and I realized I didn't want to control the world, I just wanted to live my life in peace. Alaska is the only place where a man can find peace, but it's getting harder. Sometimes you have to look for it."

"Did you ever see UFOs in Vietnam?"

"Many times, when we were on patrol or in battle, I saw UFOs. Not interfering, just observing. We had a sergeant who used to say every time we went on a mission, 'Some men are the windshield; some are the bugs.' It's an expression that haunts my days and nights. I just made sure I wasn't one of the bugs and tried to keep my true feelings to myself. While I often woke up in the middle of the night with that expression pounding in my ears, it was that same expression that helped me when I encountered the lizards."

"Can you tell me about your encounter?" I asked.

"We have stories, old stories about the lizard men," he began. "One of my fondest memories is my daddy telling me stories about the men with tails who once visited Earth and even established villages. They were cannibals and often kidnapped people. One day the villagers, tired of losing their relatives, came up with a way to kill them. They waited until they entered their homes—they lived in caves. They blocked the entrance and set it on fire. Killed all of them. When more lizard men came from the stars, they found their dead relatives and never came back again."

"But you said you met them. How do explain that?"

"I think they're back."

"Where did you have your encounter?" I asked.

"I always go back to the islands for the hunting season. My family still lives there, and it's my way of connecting. When Dad was alive, I went hunting with him. We always had a big celebration after the hunt, and Dad and I were honored as veterans. I miss him a lot. He helped me get through my PTSD. He was my best counselor. Because of Dad, I can function like a man. Because of the lizard men, I'm on a new mission."

"Was it after you were discharged that you saw the lizard men?" I asked.

"No. I came home on furlough. Dad and I went on a hunt. That's when we saw them. My dad isn't here to verify my story, but I swear to you, it is true."

"When did you encounter them?"

"As I said, we were hunting. It was extremely cold that day, colder than usual. The wind picked up early, and as the day progressed it got stronger. Ominous clouds moved in and we decided to go home. As we packed up the dog sleds, the snow began to swirl in a circular motion like a whirlwind. It became so strong that we had to hold onto the sleds and each other to stay upright. Then just as it suddenly began, it stopped, and that's when we saw the spacecraft. It was a long cylinder, dark gray machine. At first glance, it looked like a submarine, but it was no submarine."

"How big was it?"

"Maybe sixty feet long and about half that size around."

"Do you mean thirty feet high?" I asked.

"Yes. It made the ice unstable. Part of it was hanging into the water. I remember fearing we would lose our footing, and I told my father we had to get to safety."

"How were the dogs reacting?"

"Growling and barking. We finally got them organized and gave the command for them to head toward home, but before they could move, we saw them."

"The lizard men?"

"Yes. There were two of them. At first, they didn't see us. They had their backs to us as they descended the craft. They moved away from the craft and began cutting blocks of ice."

"What did they do with the ice blocks?"

"They had some kind of a conveyer. After they finished cutting the blocks they moved them to their ship. That's when they saw us. They came toward us, and my father pointed his gun at them. A flash of light came out of one of their arms and the gun flew into the air."

"What did you do?"

"I was paralyzed. I couldn't move. The next thing I remember, we're on board the craft. There were four of them in the room. My dad was stoic, not responding to them. I struck at the one closest to me, but he stood like a rock, unmoving. I understood that they cared nothing for humans, and if we fought, we would never see our families again. It was a sickening threat that overwhelmed me."

"Do you remember how you reacted to that?"

"I kept repeating in my mind, my old Sarge's mantra, 'Some men are windshields, some men are bugs,' and I decided at that moment I would survive. I don't remember much after that. My Dad says that he saw them insert a needle in my neck. I don't remember that. The next thing we knew, we were back on the ice and the dogs were eager to go home. I remember turning in the direction of the spacecraft, and that's when I saw it rise maybe twenty feet off the ice, and then it dove under the sea and disappeared."

"Do you mean the spacecraft went under the water?"

"Yes, I think they live under the ocean. In the old days, the stories say that they never saw the men with tails again after their village was destroyed. They told that they came from the sky, but maybe they came from under the water. Maybe they have a whole civilization under the sea."

"Did your dad remember anything?"

"Much more than I did. Dad said they put me to sleep and took me away. Later they returned me and took him. Dad recalled being placed in a glass box and a cone placed over his head. He said he felt like they were trying to steal his soul. I assumed they did the same thing to me. When they released the cone, he said he collapsed to the floor. After that, he found himself beside me on the ice."

"Can you describe the lizard men?" I asked.

"I call them lizard men because they looked like lizards. Their faces were like lizards or snakes, but they don't crawl like lizards, they walk upright. They had a brownish face with a flat nose. I saw no outside ears, only holes, but their mouths were wide like a lizard and wrapped around the sides of their snake faces. I do believe they were cannibals. I have no proof, but Dad remembered seeing what appeared to be dismembered bodies. I saw no such thing, but it frightened my father so much that he never hunted unless he was with a group."

"Were they human bodies?"

"My dad thought so."

"What about their skin?" I asked.

"Scales. Like a snake or fish. It was splotched. Like a green and tan. When they moved the color changed. It was very strange. There was a darker brown stripe down their backs to the tip of their tails."

"Tails?"

"Oh yes, they had tails. They were just like the old stories. They had tails."

"Can you describe them physically?"

"They towered over us. I'd say they were probably seven feet tall. They had strong, muscular arms. Their legs were short but muscular. Their middle part was covered in some kind of a leather vest, but I saw no buttons. I think they must have been attached in the back some way. Their tails were huge. They used it to thrust themselves forward so they appeared to hop instead of walk. They had no necks. When I looked at them from behind, the top of their heads to their tails was continuous. No neck. I focused on the fact they were bugs and we had to be smarter. Bugs aren't smarter than humans."

"Did they communicate anything to you?"

"No, but as I said, I got a clear message that humans meant nothing to them. I believe that is true. When villagers are lost at sea today, I think it is the lizard men. They are still alive and operate under the ocean. I think they take humans to their underground homes and eat them."

"How did that encounter change your life?"

"Now I know the truth. The legends of my father and grandfathers are true. When I go back to the village, I always tell the children the old stories, and I end it with my personal encounter. I warn them to be careful of the lizard men. As for me, I live in fear that someday they will come back and destroy our villages, but there is nothing I can do about it. I guess you'd say the experience made me feel more vulnerable. I hadn't felt that way since I was in 'Nam."

"Yes, but it sounds like you are the windshield," I said.

He nodded and smiled.

I have not seen Al since we talked that one day in the Veteran's Center. But I have met other Vietnam veterans who remind me of him. I stopped to help a veteran one day who was begging near the Walmart in Bozeman. He smiled as I handed him a five-dollar bill. As I walked away, he called out across the street to another homeless veteran and yelled, "Some men are the windshields, some are the bugs." I paused for a moment and looked in his direction. He waved at me and smiled broadly. I wanted to go to him and ask him if he knew Al, but before I could react, I saw him climb into a battered van and disappear.

11. RUSSELL'S STORY:
THE MAN WITH WINGS

In the November 16, 1966, issue of the West Virginia Point Pleasant Register, an article appeared entitled "Couples See Man-Sized Bird...Creature...Something." It revealed the story of two young couples who encountered a large white creature whose eyes "glowed red." They described the creature as a "large flying man with ten-foot wings" that followed their car while they were driving outside of town near the site of a former World War II munitions plant. The creature became widely known as Mothman. In this chapter, you will meet Russell, a friend from college, who grew up on the Elk River, an area where the man with wings was frequently sighted. Although he had confided in me decades earlier that he had seen the flying man, he had never gone public with his sighting

I first met Russell during the week of freshman orientation at the university where we were both the recipients of four-year college scholarships. Russell, who spoke in a backwoods, substandard twang associated with hillbillies, was often the brunt of jokes and teasing from our peers. Although he was handsome, his weathered briefcase, baggy pants, and oversized corduroy sports jacket established him as an unorthodox individual, unacceptable in "cool" circles or fraternity cliques. Russell, who also traced his roots to the Cherokee/Choctaw nations, was my friend; our friendship has lasted through time.

When we graduated, Russell and I took teaching jobs at the same high school; he taught math, I taught English. At the end of our first year, Russell's contract was not renewed. Just as in college, he had become the object of student jokes, tauntings, and pranks. When he moved on, we lost touch. I had not seen him for more than four decades, but with the miracle of the internet, he contacted me after my first book was published. I learned that he had worked at NASA and for a non-profit group known as the Institute of Aeronautical Science, and then as a private consultant to many astronomical and aeronautical organizations and private companies. When he learned of my planned cross-country road trip, he invited me to visit him.

I arrived at Russell's house on Sunday morning at 11:00 a.m. When the door opened, he greeted me with a massive bear hug. "How long has it been?" he asked. "What happened to you anyway? You just disappeared from the face of the earth." His familiar prattle, which I always chalked up to nervousness, continued as he led me through the house to the kitchen. "Sit yourself down. I was fixing to make some coffee."

I watched as he busied himself at the stove, adjusting the burner as coffee began to percolate. Moments later, he placed two antique cups and saucers on the table and poured the black brew from an equally ancient coffeepot. As I listened to his nonstop questions and comments, I realized that in all of these years, he had not lost his backwoods twang, or his unfashionable style, and yet, he made no apologies for himself. That quality had endeared him to me when I was a student and his colleague, and that feeling had not changed. I still admired the man who marched to a different drummer, and yet I couldn't help but wonder how the years of verbal abuse had not impacted his life.

For the next two hours, we caught up on our lives. In the early afternoon, Russell ushered me to the back porch, located on the north side of his house. "This is the place I watch the stars," he declared as he pointed to a huge telescope encased in a wooded viewing tower. "That's the reason I live here in the country away from lights. I can view the night sky without interference."

"Do you believe in UFOs?" I asked.

"Without a doubt."

"You once told me, many years ago, that you had an encounter?"

"I told you back in college about the man with wings," he answered.

I nodded. "I remember the stories about the Mothman as if it were yesterday."

"My family has lived in the Elk River area of West Virginia since the early 1800s. There've always been strange creatures sighted in these hills. My cousin Eugene and I saw the flying man, as we called him, one afternoon by the railroad tracks. He wasn't no big moth."

"What do you think it was?"

"An astronaut from another world," he replied.

"Can you tell me about your encounter?"

"Eugene and I were walking the tracks in search of coal dropped by the passing trains. We were poor and gathering free coal that fell from the coal trains was a regular chore for us. It was dirty work, but we used coal to heat our house. We loaded our bags and headed down the tracks toward home, when suddenly we heard a strange whirring sound followed by strong wind, which forced us forward, causing us to drop our gunny sacks. As we struggled to pick up the coal that had fallen out of our bags, we saw a white, man-like figure descend from the sky." He paused for a moment, finished off his coffee and poured another cup. "He was at least ten feet tall with a wingspan at least that big. He tried to communicate with us."

"What do you mean?"

"He made an unrecognizable chattering sound more reminiscent of an animal than human, but higher pitched, almost squeaky at times."

"What did you do?" I asked.

"I asked him who he was and where he came from."

"And?"

"He kept chattering, and suddenly in almost a look of frustration, he flew upward toward the clouds and disappeared."

"Did you ever see him again?"

"No, only for that brief moment."

"Can you describe him?" I asked.

"He had a human form. He was easily ten feet tall. He was all white. By that I mean, the suit he wore was white. It was not a material I was familiar with. It shimmered. It's hard to explain it. His eyes, his pupils I should say, appeared red, almost like an animal caught in headlights. He had no visible hair. His body was covered from head to toe with his glowing suit. When he stood before us, his wings folded behind him and you really couldn't tell he had wings."

"Do you think his wings were a part of his body or something attached to help him fly."

"I believe the latter, at least now I do. When I saw him as a teenager, that thought never occurred to me. Now I think it was an astronaut suit but not our kind. Although they looked like wings, I believe he manipulated the wings with his arms and hands. They were definitely mechanical."

"Can you tell me how you know that?"

"While his body suit was form fitting, unlike the astronaut's suits, his arms contained some type of equipment. I remember not quite understanding it at the time, but today I believe he had an operation device—like a mini-computer—that allowed him to control his wings."

"Do you think the flying man was an alien?" I asked.

"I know he was an alien. Shortly after we saw him, we saw a silver streak glistening in the sun. It was plain as day. We saw a circular craft fly upward with enormous speed and disappear."

"What is your assessment of the encounter?"

"Back then, Eugene and I were teenagers. We didn't have the technical advances we have today. We didn't know about computers. We'd heard of flying saucers, but most people connected them up to comic book science fiction. When I remember the encounter today, I look at it through a scientist's eyes, and I know the man with wings was from outer space. There is no question."

"Can you tell me anything else about his appearance?"

"The most amazing thing was his height. I am five feet eleven.

He towered over me by at least four feet. He tried desperately to communicate with us, but neither of us could understand him. He really looked human except for the eyes. I believe there are many living entities in the universe that are far advanced to us. We hear about the small aliens with big eyes—and they do exist—or the tall whites who appear loving and caring, but we don't hear so much about the others —others that don't take human shape or the giants or the hairy men who visit." He paused and leaned against the banister circling his deck. "Even our old legends speak about men with wings and men who were ten or twelve feet tall. You know the legends. Our grandparents told us those legends, and they weren't mythology or folklore. They told of actual events in our tribal history. The flying men were common on earth in our great, great, great grandfather's time. And they were not angels. They were men from other worlds."

"How do you know all of these things?"

"I've worked in the aerospace industry for five decades. I have talked with astronauts. I've seen things with my own eyes. I can't reveal the sources, but I know they exist. I just can't reveal too much because of my sworn oath of silence."

"In other words, you do believe that many different, intelligent life forms exist elsewhere in the universe."

"I've always believed the possibility existed from the stories of the elders."

"I knew the old legends, too, and I believed, as you, in the possibility. You worked for NASA. What can you tell me about NASA? Do they know that UFOs are real and that there is other life in the universe?" I asked.

"NASA knows. I can tell you that even though UFOs are accepted by the public, 'real scientists' are still not willing to identify themselves publicly as believers, for fear of criticism from their peers. Yet they know. Pilots know, astronauts know, people in the government know, and even our elders know. Space aliens exist and they monitor us on Earth and in space. And I do believe there are some species that use humans for their experiments. They have no regard for human life."

"Have you ever heard astronauts talk about UFOs?" I asked.

"Several times. Scientists and astronauts talk about UFOs in confidential conversations. They just don't do it publicly. At least twelve astronauts have stated they saw UFOs while in space. NASA Astronaut Neil Armstrong said the aliens have a base on the Moon and told them in no uncertain terms to get off and stay off the Moon. Both Neil Armstrong a Buzz Aldrin saw UFOs shortly after their landing on the Moon. NASA hides all of this or calls it conspiracy theories and the public buys it."

"Why do you think the government is so secretive?"

"They believe that admission would cause a panic. That's the official word, but the truth is that if they admit it, the people are more likely to lose faith in a government that has been lying to the public for almost seven decades. That's why your book is important. I've actually received messages from several scientists and astronauts about your work. They are very excited about it. So your books are not going unnoticed. That reminds me, before you leave, I want to give you a couple of names of elders you should contact in the hills. They have some interesting stories to tell. You might want to include them in a future book."

"Thank you. But why do you believe the star visitors have never revealed themselves to the world?"

"I believe that our Mother Earth is too young and humans too primitive to be of much interest to them other than for experimental purposes. But I think they watch us all the time."

"Why?"

"I believe they fear that we may do something to harm the universe in our childish stupidity. So they keep an eye on us, not protectively, but to make sure we don't destroy the Earth in our quest to destroy one another."

"What do you mean by that?" I asked.

"Have you ever considered what a desirable place the Earth is? While I don't think humans are a priority, I believe the planet is important to them. I don't think they're waiting to ferry us up to the sky to protect us. They've already cloned humans. It's more likely the planet would be far more valuable to them without humans. The Earth is a remarkable place, a rare gem in the cosmos."

"Are you saying the planet is what they want?"

"It could be. I think they test our pilots and astronauts to learn our capability. I know they abduct humans, clone them, and test them to discover any uniqueness and weakness. It may be that they will let us kill most of the Earth's population, and then they can make their move. Maybe one day they will get tired of waiting and invade us."

"What are the chances of that, do you think?"

"50/50."

"Aren't you concerned what the government might do to you if I publish what you are revealing to me?"

"Sure, I've thought about it, but I refuse to live my life in fear. There are too many lies. It is time that humans unite because it may be that we face a far greater threat from space than we face from each other."

"So President Reagan had it right," I said, "when he made that statement at the UN."

"Not only did he have it right, I think he issued a warning, although cloaked, but a warning. We just didn't realize the enormity of the warning."

"What about your cousin, Eugene? How did he handle the experience?"

"Eugene," he said slowly. "God rest his soul. He died a few months ago from a stroke. He never got over the experience. He started carrying guns all the time. He rarely went out of the house. Aunt Rub, his mother, took care of him. The day I left for college he pleaded with me to stay. He felt I'd deserted him. I always felt guilty about that." He paused and stared into his empty coffee cup. "He always waited for the star man to return. He carried guns to kill him."

"Kill him?"

He nodded.

"But isn't that the way? Humans have a way of destroying what they don't understand."

"What about you? You've been successful. You were not affected like your cousin."

"I was a mathematician. Math was my comfort zone. I didn't have to deal with people. Working in space-related fields gave me an escape and allowed me to be close to what we know about other life forms in space. Eugene found comfort in guns; I used math."

After dinner, Russell and I walked along the railroad track where he had seen the Star Man. The tracks were still used, but there were no coal trains anymore. Just sleek computerized engines carrying goods to Wal-Mart and grocery stores.

"The trains don't stop here no more," Russell said. "West Virginia is a disposable state. It's too bad. West Virginians watch the night sky. They see things and they have stories to tell, but it's not likely they will ever tell anyone. As a whole they don't trust the government."

When I left Russell that evening, I felt conflicted. Russell confirmed what I already knew; life did exist beyond Earth, and the flying astronaut was just one example of the many species that live out there. When I invited Russell to visit me in Montana, he told me that he seldom traveled. The internet has changed the way he works; he now conducts his professional activities from home. He felt it was important to stay close to home and prepare for whatever might occur. He told me should the time come when an event would potentially occur that could change the world, he would email me with the words, "Alas, Babylon," the code for an impending apocalyptic event used in Pat Frank's book of the same name. "Alas, Babylon" seems like an appropriate alert. In the meantime, I am happy to report that Russell and I keep in touch weekly via email and phone.

12. BUCK'S STORY: THEY'RE THE DEVIL'S CHILDREN

Buck, whose legal name was Horatio, a moniker given to him by a Catholic nun at a boarding school in South Dakota, worked as a legal aide for an advocacy group representing American Indians in federal prison. As a liaison with the prison and trusted by both the incarcerated and incarcerators, Buck spent most days investigating the stories of the convicts and preparing briefs for lawyers for appeals. I caught up with Buck during a visit to his grandmother's house. He explained that he kept his encounters private due to the nature of his work. He felt his encounters, if made public, would be fuel to discredit him, and his work was too important to jeopardize it.

I had been friends with Myrtle, Buck's grandmother, for many years. She was one of the first Indian teachers on the reservation. Over the years we became friends. It was Myrtle who convinced Buck to study pre-law at the university. While lack of money and family obligations put an end to his goal of becoming a lawyer, Buck appeared content in his role of advocacy. As we sat around Myrtle's cramped kitchen table enjoying herbal tea, Buck talked passionately about his work and the injustice in the state.

"In South Dakota," he explained, "Indians make up sixty percent of the federal caseload, and yet we are only eight-and-a half percent of the total population. Now, do you call that justice or racism? It's the same in all the states with an Indian minority: North Dakota, Montana, Minnesota, Oklahoma. There is no justice."

He set down his teacup and looked at me. A smile crossed his face, and then he reached for my hand. "Sorry, sister. I know you didn't come to hear about the prison system. You're here for another purpose. UFOs and aliens. So where do I begin. I've had more than a half dozen encounters."

"You could start at the beginning," I said.

Buck looked at his grandmother, and she nodded.

"Well, that would be when I was about nine years old. I was staying with MawMaw," he said, indicating Myrtle. "I did that a lot. She was my rock." He looked at her and smiled affectionately. "At night, I began seeing these monster men who often roamed around MawMaw's house at night. I was a night owl boy—had a hard time sleeping, and the summers were so hot, and in the evenings, it was hard to sleep. We had one fan in the house and it was reserved for the living room. At night I would go there, relax on the couch, and quietly turn on the fan. MawMaw didn't allow me to use the fan much. She said it ran up her electric bill, and in those days even being a teacher didn't pay much. The tribe set the salaries, and teachers were at the low end of the totem pole."

"Can you tell me about the monster men you saw?" I asked.

"I saw them the first time when I was a boy, but every encounter has been with the ones I call the monster men. They are the same."

"What can you tell me about the encounters?" I asked.

"Always before I saw them," he said, "I would see a bright light that lit up the night sky and the earth below. It gave the appearance of a bank of bright lights, all pointed at the windows of the house. After that the monster men came. I would watch them as they walked around at night. I would see their shadows as they passed the windows. I was afraid. It took at least several weeks before I got the courage to go outside and check them out. At first, I hid in the shadows, and what I observed were really monsters. They were taller than any man I had ever seen. They walked funny, like when they set their foot down, it came down with a thud. They seemed strange to me. Like someone learning to walk for the first time. They walked a lot like toddlers who were unsure of their balance, but they were huge beings walking like that. To a nine year old this was confusing, but at the same time I was fascinated. I wanted to know where these monsters came from. I wondered if they were demons from hell that the Father talked about in church."

"Did you ever reveal yourself to them?" I asked.

"I did, but not on purpose. One night, I heard a frightful sound coming from the barn. I knew something was scaring my mare, Betty. I heard her kicking her stall and neighing loudly. I rushed out the door only to come within a foot of one of the monsters. He reached down and caught me in one hand and held me aloft like a rag doll. He sniffed me. He actually stiffed me like an animal might do when they are unsure of something. Then he dropped me from his grasp and walked toward another monster who was about twenty feet away. I jumped to my feet and headed for the barn."

"Was anyone else in the house while all of this was going on?" I asked.

"MawMaw, but she was asleep and didn't wake up." He reached out and held Myrtle's hand.

"Did you make it to the barn?" I asked.

"I did. When I entered the barn, I picked up my BB gun that I always kept by the door. I didn't expect it would stop the monsters, but I could at least put one's eye out. I was a good shot. That's how I got the name Buck. I could always be counted on to bag the biggest buck when deer hunting."

"Were there any monsters in the barn?" I asked.

"I didn't see any, but I smelled them. They had a terrible stench about them like rotten eggs. They were there and gone I guess. I tried to calm Betty, but nothing could comfort her. I finally gave up."

"Can you describe the monster who grabbed you?"

"At the time, I couldn't see much. It was dark, but two weeks later they returned. This time, I was ready. I had my 12-gauge, a box of shells, and my flashlight. After the first encounter, I was ready."

He paused while Myrtle filled his tea cup with hot water. "I was so naive," he said.

"What happened?"

"It was along about midnight. At the sign of the first lights, I went outside and climbed into the loft of the barn. It wasn't long until I saw this long tank-like craft descend from the sky and land. I saw four beings emerge from the craft and walk toward the small creek that flowed on the west side of the property. A few minutes passed, and they began walking the property, making what appeared to be a circle around the place. It was like they were searching for something."

"Was there anything special about your property?" I asked. "Any minerals, rocks, or something they would want?"

"Geodes. Tons of geodes, on the ground, under the ground. Our property was on the site of an ancient riverbed. Lots of geodes. I loved cracking them open and bringing them home to MawMaw." He pointed to a shelf along the ceiling of the small kitchen. "That's a part of my collection. I don't know why they would be interested in geodes. They did not appear to be beings that were interested in the aesthetic."

"What can you tell me about them?"

"They reminded me in some ways of a huge snake, at least their heads did. Their body was more human, with arms and legs. They seemed to be able to communicate with one another, but I could not understand them. They made hissing and grunting sounds. It was nothing I understood, but it looked like they understood each other. Their heads were huge, like the size of a buffalo head, but there was no neck. Just a head that grew out of their body. When one of them came close to the barn, I shined by flashlight in his face, and he had the weirdest eyes, big slanted eyes that reflected red in the light like a wild animal. His mouth was like a big snout, nothing like a human. When he opened his mouth in response to the light, I realized he could eat me with one bite. The light in his face caused him to back away, and I fired a shot. Not directly at him, but close enough that he knew I meant business. To this day, I remember the sound of the shot, the kick of the 12-gauge, and what I interpreted as fear in the reaction of the monster man. At once, he headed toward the others who had assembled together in a circle. For a moment they stood there. Then they walked back to their spacecraft and disappeared. I watched them leave. I stayed in the loft until they were no more than a star in the sky."

"Have you had any other encounters with the monster men?" I asked.

"Several. It is always here on this property. I worry about MawMaw who refuses to leave this house. But they are explorers, nothing more. I have since learned they come for the quartz. I don't know what they do with it, but as I understand it, it is a valued commodity in the universe."

"So you have communicated with them."

"Only on a nominal basis. They can plant ideas in my head. I don't think they mean any harm, but they do not want to reveal themselves to humans. They fear humans will try to destroy them."

"Now that you have communicated with them and seen them on more than one occasion, can you tell me anything else about them?"

"On this planet, I think they would be considered relatives of the lizard. Their appearance from mid-torso to their heads is very lizard like. They do not have scales, but they have a translucent skin that looks brown and green at the same time. From their torso down, they have these huge legs making it difficult to walk. Their arms are monstrous where they join their bodies, but then taper off to small claw like hands. It reminds me of pictures I've seen of dinosaurs. Maybe they are a mix of dinosaurs and lizards. It is hard to describe something that doesn't exist, at least not on this planet."

"Do you believe they are of superior intelligence?"

"That's obvious, isn't it? If not, how do they come here? They are definitely intelligent, and it would be hard for humans to accept that these monstrous lizard men are smarter than they. They are also carnivorous. I've seen them capture and eat deer while the deer was still alive. So they are powerful, too. Humans would not stand a chance with them in combat."

"So why do you remain silent?"

"Who would believe me? Maybe you and MawMaw, who has seen them too."

I looked at Myrtle, she nodded and got up and went to the water cooler and added water to her teakettle.

"Do you have anything you can add to Buck's story?" I asked, addressing Myrtle.

She nodded and then quietly said: "They're the Devil's children. God didn't make those creatures."

I see Buck frequently. When I visit Myrtle and he is staying overnight, we often talk late into the night about his work and the monster men. There is no question in my mind that Buck is a reliable and honest observer of the reptilian creatures that have been reported by others. While his encounters do not seem to terrify the adult Buck, it is obvious that as a little nine-year-old boy he was terrified of the monster men.

SECTION 3

OTHER STAR PEOPLE

1. OTHER STAR PEOPLE: INTRODUCTION

In *2001: A Space Odyssey*, Arthur C. Clark explored the idea that highly advanced alien intelligences would be indistinguishable from gods. When Europeans first arrived in the Americas, many indigenous people took them to be gods. They had the ability to do unimaginable things far removed from the reality of the indigenous people. Their origin was uncertain. They had arrived on enormous ships and had the ability to kill with thunderous weapons. They differed in appearance from the indigenous people, and they wore unfamiliar clothing.

Today, space travelers might appear to us in the same way that the Europeans appeared to Native people. They might do unimaginable things. They might travel over vast distances of space using energy unknown to us. They might communicate using telepathy, vanish (dematerialize), and teleport themselves. They could possess powerful, unfamiliar weapons or medical knowledge that might make modern humans seem like cave dwellers. They might be able to manipulate human brains, control movements and behavior, and erase memories. Through advanced science and technology, they might be able to clone individuals or create new life forms. At the present time, our technology is not advanced enough to be able to perform these feats, but these hindrances are the result of our current knowledge, and it is likely that Star People travelling over the vast distances of space would be our superiors both intellectually and technologically.

Many supernatural abilities have been attributed to the Star People, including shapeshifting, telekinesis, teleportation, telepathy, DNA replication, biological manipulation, possessing superhuman physical and mental powers, and creating life forms (hybrids and clones). Healing or increasing human intellectual abilities have also been attributed to the Star People.

While UFO healings are not new, they have received little coverage until UFO investigator Preston Dennett's wrote *UFO Healings* in 1996. In the book, he details more than one hundred cases of individuals cured by UFO encounters, everything from blindness to cancer. UFO investigators and doctors have verified all these cases. Prior to Dennett's groundbreaking book, Budd Hopkins, Dr. David Jacobs, and Dr. John Mack—three leading UFO abduction experts—reported that extraterrestrials healed individuals.

Well-known UFO investigators such as Brad Steiger, Dr. Richard Boylan, Kevin Randle, Jacques Vallee, and Timothy Green Beckley have also investigated UFO healing cases. Dr. Edith Fiore maintained that one half of her clients had experienced UFO healings.

Thomas Bullard reported that of the two-hundred-and-seventy abduction accounts in his study, there were thirteen cases of UFO healings. According to Bullard, "The other and more cheerful side of permanent aftereffects are the thirteen instances where the witness left the abduction healed of some ailment...many of the cures appear to result from deliberate intervention."

A few websites list "celestial healings" and UFO healings on the internet. John Hunter Gray, Chairman of the Indian Studies Department at the University of North Dakota, who identified himself as a half-breed with Micmac/Abenaki/Mohawk Indian heritage, reported two UFO encounters with his son. An outspoken advocate of the benefits of the encounters, Gray said: "I state candidly and at the outset that I see ET visitors, the so-called alien humanoids, as friendly and with positive motivations and beneficial effects. I am inclined to see them as essentially one race, quite similar to ourselves in many ways, but a good jump ahead evolution-wise." He said that he and his son have received positive physical enhancements as a result of his encounters, including "...

faster rate of hair growth, thicker and darker eyebrows, faster nail growth, quicker rate of healing for cuts and scratches, cessation of bleeding gums, fading of old scarring, improved skin tone, improved circulation, more energy, and enhanced immunity."

Native American legends tell stories of healings by people from the sky. One of the more famous legends speak of a young man who was thrown over a cliff by his so-called friends. With a broken leg, he was unable to climb out of the small canyon. The Thunder Men from the sky healed him and took him to live with them in the sky where he became a very powerful Thunderer.

During the course of my interviews over a period of thirty-five plus years, I have met many individuals who have experienced amazing healings or miracles. In this section, you will read about extraordinary healings, ranging from improved intellectual ability to overcoming addiction. Two of the most unusual miracles reported involved animals. You will also read about encounters that describe supernatural or superhuman powers possessed by the Star People.

2. ADDIE AND TANSY'S STORY: WE'RE SPACE AGE INDIANS

Addie and Tansy grew up together on the reservation. Their parents owned adjoining ranches. The girls were unstoppable on the rodeo circuit and were state and regional barrel-racing and calf-roping champions. Aside from their rodeo pursuits, they enjoyed horseback riding and camping, writing music, surfing the internet, and staying in touch with friends and relatives on social media. They often took their horses for three-day weekends in the hills around their homes. It was on one such trip that they had a most unusual encounter.

"Our favorite camping spot is over the buttes there," Addie said as she pointed west to a secluded spot in a low valley surrounded by hills. "The site is protected from the wind and there is a small pond and plenty of grass for the horses. Trees grow along the south side of the pond, and we pitch our tent under the trees and spend our time surfing the net, making videos on our cell phones, writing music, and going on long rides."

"We take enough food to feed an army," said Tansy, laughing. "Our life might sound boring to other girls our age, but we wouldn't want another. It's total freedom."

"How many people can say that?" Addie interjected.

I looked at the high school juniors sitting next to each other on a weathered log bench next to Addie's horse corral. They could have passed for twins. They were both about five feet seven and trim. They looked like they worked out daily in a gym, but neither professed to such activities. They claimed that working the ranch and lifting hay bales kept them strong and in shape. Addie wore her hair in braids, which hung nearly to her waist. Tansy's thick black hair was pulled back in a ponytail. They were beautiful girls, but the most beautiful thing about them was that they didn't seem to know it. Their joy for life, their humor, and their love for their horses, their family, and each other would have made any parent burst with pride.

"I understand the two of you are champions on the rodeo circuit," I said. "Can you tell me about that?"

"Addie's the best barrel racer in the whole tri-state region," Tansy said. "She has a room-full of trophies. I'm second best, but I prefer calf-roping."

"Are you girls competitive with each other?"

"Not with each other," Addie said, "just everyone else. Tansy and I are like sisters. We were sixteen last week, and we celebrated our birthday together with our families. We were born on the same day; I'm the oldest by five hours."

"Addie, your mother told me that the two of you had an encounter with the Star People on one of your camping trips recently. Can you tell me about that?"

"It was more than an encounter. It was a kidnapping, if you know what I mean."

"Please tell me the details of what happened to you."

"Our kidnapping happened last year," Tansy said.

"So you were fifteen at the time; is that correct?"

They both nodded.

"It was a Friday afternoon when we packed our horses for the trip," Addie said. "There were some clouds moving in from the west, but we decided to go anyway. We'd camped out in rain, and we weren't going to let a few clouds keep us from our weekly campout."

"It was going to be our last camping trip until Thanksgiving weekend," said Tansy. "School was going to start the following week." She paused for a moment and opened a stick of gum offering one to Addie and me.

"When we arrived at our spot," said Addie, "we hurried to put up the tent and put all of our food and belongings inside. While

I gathered firewood, Tansy set about starting a fire. We brought some chili my mom made, and we planned to heat it up for dinner."

"I had crackers, chocolate, and marshmallows for smores," Tansy interrupted. "We came prepared." The girls looked at each other, nodded, and laughed.

"When did the Star People arrive?" I asked.

The girls looked at each other. Tansy looked to Addie, who took a deep breath and said: "It was several hours later. As the evening grew dark—it gets dark about seven now—the clouds became more threatening, and when the first clap of thunder came, followed by lightening, we checked on the horses and decided to go inside the tent."

"Not long after," Tansy said, "the rains came. It was a downpour and only lasted a few minutes. After the storm, we crawled out of the tent, checked on the horses, and tried to save our fire, which still had red hot embers."

"Once we got the fire going again," Addie said, "we decided to take the horses to the pond for a drink. We got the flashlights, mounted the horses bareback, and headed for the water. We no sooner headed toward the pond than a bright light came down from the sky and shined directly on top of us." Addie looked at Tansy, who reached for her hand and held it. "The horses became frightened and started to run toward the pond. It was all we could do to hold on."

"The light followed us," said Tansy, "wherever we went. I looked upward trying to figure out where the light was coming from and it blinded me." Tansy paused, looked at Addie, put her arm around her shoulders, and Addie nodded as though telling her to continue. When Tansy remained silent, Addie took over.

"Suddenly, I had the strangest feeling. Everything went silent. There were no animal sounds, no tree sounds, not even the sound of the horses drinking. It was like everything on Earth, at least in our little spot, stood still. I didn't even have a chance to mention it to Tansy when all of a sudden we were airborne."

"When you say you were airborne, does that mean you were

taken upward toward the light?" I asked.

"Not just us," Tansy said, "our horses too. I remember looking down at the pond and hanging on for dear life. The horses went limp. I hugged Juniper around the neck and clung to him. I felt dizzy and was afraid I would fall off. There would be no one to rescue me."

"Starwood was lifeless, too," said Addie. "I placed my head on his, but I thought he was dead. Then I thought maybe the four of us were dead. I remember screaming as loud as I could, but there was no one to hear me, not even Tansy, who appeared as lifeless as Juniper."

"The next thing we knew," said Tansy, "we were in a huge, strange room. We clung to our horses' necks, and when we sat up, we saw several short, skinny little people approaching us. They were the strangest people I had ever seen."

"They were bald with huge black eyes, and they were not wearing any clothes," said Addie. "They had the strangest skin, kind of rubbery looking. Their coloring was strange. I screamed again, and I think I passed out because when I came to Tansy and I were on tables in another room. My first thought was for Starwood. I wanted to know where my horse was. I loved my horse, and I thought they had done something with him. I yelled at them, but they just stood there staring at me."

"Do you remember what happened next?" I asked.

"That's when these tall men came into the room," said Addie. "They looked like humans, and I yelled at them and demanded to know where we were. I wanted to know about Starwood."

"What did they look like?" I asked.

"They were tall and skinny," Tansy said. "They looked like pale, hungry humans who had been locked up somewhere without any sun. Their hair was very thin. They had long faces, and but their skin was so white I thought they were ghosts."

"They looked like women," Addie said, "but I think they were men. Very dainty. I couldn't tell if they were men or women."

Tansy interrupted: "They were dressed in funny white suits

with a blue band around their arms. One of them approached us and told us that the horses were okay and that we would be okay."

"Did he speak orally to you?"

"I never thought about it," Addie said. "I just knew they were okay."

"Me, too," said Tansy. "His manner calmed me. I felt like I was with a friend." Addie looked at Tansy who nodded in agreement.

"So what happened next?" I asked.

"They took blood samples, a strand of our hair, and scraped our skin," said Tansy. "But they inserted something in us. I don't know how to describe it. It was a glass tube or a glass needle of some kind. I'd never seen an instrument like that. It was a long object. I screamed when I saw it, but one of the tall ones said it would not hurt."

"I tried to relax," Addie said, "but I was frightened, too. I don't like doctors and I think they were doctors."

"Where did they insert the tube?" I asked.

"In my stomach, close to my navel," said Addie. As if prompted, both girls pulled up their t-shirts and displayed a round, red mark about the size of a dime. I moved closer and examined it. They were identical in size, shape, and placement, and reminded me of a blood-blister I once had as a child.

"That's the mark they left on us. It's never gone away," said Tansy.

"And it's been a year," Addie reminded me.

"Did it hurt?"

"No, we felt nothing," said Tansy. "They said it wouldn't hurt and it didn't, but it won't go away. It's a constant reminder."

The girls looked at each other and nodded in agreement.

"They marked us forever," said Addie. "After that, they said we were too young and that we should come with them. Those little freaky guys came, held us by the arm, and took us to our horses."

"Then suddenly," Tansy said, "we were back on Earth, sitting on our horses as though nothing ever happened. As the horses drank from the pond, a clap of thunder filled the night, and we looked up and saw the outline of a huge round object lift upward and disappear in a flash of lightning. I don't think we slept a wink that night. We sat up talking about what happened to us."

"Did you stay the weekend at your camping spot?" I asked.

"Oh, yes," they said in unison.

"No little ugly men or tall white men could keep us from our weekend," said Tansy. "I think our age saved us. They said we were too young for childbearing."

"I think they discovered we were virgins," Addie said, "and they stopped their tests on us."

"Why do you think that?" I asked.

"Why else would we be too young?" asked Tansy. "They said they were looking for breeders. We were too young to be good breeders."

"Breeders?"

"That's what they said," Addie replied.

"I think they were looking for females to breed," Tansy said. "Just like we breed our horses. It makes me sick to think they breed people. Maybe they planned to make us pregnant. When they discovered we were just girls, they let us go. I hope they don't come back when we get older."

"If they do, we'll kick their butts," Addie said. They looked at each other and fist bumped and laughed joyously.

"Tansy, did you get the same message?" I asked.

"The message I got was we were too young." Tansy said. "We were not good specimens. That's it. But I think Addie is right. They had other plans for us but decided it was not right because of our youth."

"And they called you specimens?" I asked.

"That's the term he used," Tansy said. "He looked me in the eyes and said I was not a good specimen. While I was in their presence, it meant nothing to me, but afterwards I was angry to think they considered me, a human being, as a specimen like I think of a frog in our biology class. The teacher called the frog a specimen in our biology class."

"Have you ever heard anything so unusual?" asked Addie.

"I have never heard of anyone being abducted with their horses," I said.

"Well, there is another thing about our horses," said Tansy. "It's like a miracle. You're really going to think we're crazy, but it's like our horses are younger. We hoped they would perform with us through college, but both of us were already training a backup for Juniper and Starwood."

"But the most amazing thing happened," said Addie. "At first, we noticed changes in their ability to run and their general response to our cues as riders. But the most amazing thing was their energy levels. They had more stamina and more agility. Their response to our bodies and to our directions was amazing. It's like they could read our minds. Do you think Star Men could do something to our horses to make them mind-readers?"

"I'm not sure," I said.

"And why would they do it?" Addie asked, looking at me for an answer.

"Well, I think they did something to them," Tansy said. "They're like super-horses. They've gained a lot of attention on the rodeo circuit. Several judges have labeled them the best barrel racing and roping horses in the country. This past year, we've been offered thousands of dollars for stud services. I don't know what those Star People did, but we know the changes in Starwood and Juniper has something to do with them."

"Have you bred your horses?" I asked.

"No," Addie responded. "Our dads and grandpas think we'd better keep their newfound abilities under wraps. They want to be the first to breed them. We're just looking for the right mares."

"Do you think their super abilities might transfer to their offspring?" I asked.

"That's what we want to find out," Tansy interjected.

"Before your encounter, were the horses outstanding rodeo horses?" I asked.

"They were good horses," Tansy said, "perhaps a step above

most, but they were not super horses. I'll put it this way, they were not going to get any better. They were as good as they could be. They helped us win a lot of competitions and hopefully will get us college scholarships, but they were not the best in the world. I think now they are the best in the world."

"Did Star Men tell you anything about your horses?" I asked.

"They told us the horses were excellent specimens," said Addie, "but I was apprehensive. I didn't like the word specimens. To me, my Starwood was not a specimen. He was a part of the family. I worried they were doing tests on them like they were doing to us."

"That's a strange response. Did they elaborate on what they meant by 'excellent specimen?'" I asked.

"Nothing," Tansy said. "It's obvious they did something. The horses are different, not in temperament, but it's like they're super horses. You're going to think I'm crazy, but I always talked to Juniper. I raised him from a colt, and when I was little I called him and Addie my best friends. As I grew up, I knew he didn't understand all my chatter, but I still talked to him like he was my best friend. But now it's different. It's like he understands what I say."

"Can you give me an example?"

"Sure. Last week the wild daisies were in full bloom in that field." I followed her finger as she pointed to a large meadow." I decided I would pick a bouquet for Mom. She loves wild daisies. She says they are better than roses. So I told Juniper I wanted to pick some daisies for Mom, and he looked at me and immediately trotted off toward the meadow. I stood and watched him. It was like he knew what I was talking about. When I hesitated in following him, he sauntered further toward the field, then stopped and looked back as though he was waiting for me to follow him. He did this several times before I joined him in the meadow."

"Similar things have happened to me," Addie said. "One morning I told Starwood I wanted to pick some wild strawberries for breakfast, and he headed directly for the strawberry field without any direction from me. The trip to the wild strawberries was not a ride across the fields. It required descending several ravines to reach them in a low-lying gulch. He knew exactly where I wanted to go with no directions from me. It's like he led me; I didn't lead him."

"I wish I knew what the Star Men did to them," Tansy said. "It could change veterinary science." She paused for a moment, then looked at Addie and then at me. "You know, we're Space Age Indians. We have grown up in a world where travel to Mars will happen in our lifetime. What they did to our horses is something out of science fiction, and it has changed our lives forever. The Star Men have given us a glimpse of what the future holds for us in the space age."

After the interview, the girls spread out a picnic lunch on a barn wood table nearby. Afterwards we went to the corrals, and I met Juniper and Starwood, the miracle horses. When we arrived, the quarter horses were racing around the corral like young colts. Starwood's pinto coloring was beautiful; Juniper was a gorgeous palomino. When they saw the girls, they raced to them. While I'm not an expert on horses, there is no question that the horses appeared to understand their youthful owners before they even uttered a word.

I keep track of Addie and Tansy. Both girls plan to study animal husbandry and veterinary science when they graduate from high school. Both have been accepted to the university in a junior enrichment program. While they complete their junior and senior years in high school, they will enroll in university courses, which will give them a head start when they become college freshman. Since their abduction, they have not wavered in their belief that the Star Men changed the direction of their lives and turned their horses into super animals. Recently, they bred Starwood and Juniper with champion mares their fathers purchased from a Texas breeder. While they anxiously await the birth of their colts, I can't help but wonder if the offspring will share the traits of their fathers, and if that is the case, what will that mean for the future.

3. ELMER'S STORY:
A UFO GAVE ME A DIFFERENT LIFE

About fifteen years ago, I received a letter from my cousin, Carol, with a newspaper clipping about a collision between a UFO and a coal train in Kentucky. A year later I decided to make a trip cross-country. I planned to stop overnight to visit my cousin, and, if the occasion presented itself, to learn more about this incident. When I arrived at Carol's house, her husband informed me that she was in the hospital on life-support. When I explained I was just passing through and had just wanted to surprise Carol, he suggested a bed-and-breakfast for my overnight stay. When I checked in, a matronly woman named Ethel informed me I was her first customer from Montana since she had opened her establishment. After registering, I asked her for directions to the nearest restaurant, and she told me she had a pot roast in the oven and would be delighted if I joined her for dinner. While a believer in fate, meeting Ethel even reinforced my belief that strange things do happen in the universe that are not easily explained. The following is an account of the story about the UFO and the coal train.

At 7 p.m. I arrived promptly at the office, and Ethel welcomed me behind the counter. A hallway led to her living quarters. As we ate a delicious dinner, Ethel quizzed me about my travels. She explained that she had only been out of Kentucky once and that was for her honeymoon to Myrtle Beach.

"When I was younger, I had wanderlust, but Papa married me off young. After you get married, you put those thoughts behind you. But enough about me, I want to hear all about you and why you're traveling all by your lonesome."

"Actually, I'm on a road trip back home," I explained. "My plan was to go to my high school reunion and visit relatives. I stopped to visit my cousin, but she's in the hospital and her husband suggested your place for an overnight stay. A few years ago, she sent me news clipping about a UFO colliding with a coal train in this area. I was interested in whether anyone had seen the accident or had any other information about it. I collect stories about UFOs, and since I was driving this way, I decided to stop and follow up on it. I didn't expect to find out anything, but it was a good excuse to surprise Carol."

"Honey," said Ethel, "this is your lucky day. I know the person you should talk to. His name is Elmer. Everybody calls him the 'dumb Indian,' but he's not dumb, but he is an Indian. Then so is about twenty percent of the population around town."

We cleared the table, and Ethel busied herself, setting a new place for Elmer and making a take-home meal for his father. I was mid-way through washing dishes when I heard the kitchen door open. I came face-to-face with Elmer for the first time.

"Elmer," Ethel called out. "I want you to meet my friend. She came all the way from Montana to meet you. Have you ever met anyone from Montana?"

He shook his head and removed his baseball cap at the same time. He wiped his hand on his pants and offered it to me. Although Ethel called him a boy, Elmer appeared to be in his late thirties. He towered over the two of us. He was dressed in a plaid shirt and Dockers. His horn-rimmed glasses gave him the appearance of a professor. After we shook hands, Ethel steered him into the dining room and set a plate before him. Although I could hear them talking, I did not eavesdrop. As I finished the dishes, Ethel removed an apple pie from the oven and ordered me to join them for desert.

"Elmer was telling me that Yellowstone National Park is in Montana, and that when he was a boy he loved the cartoon character Yogi Bear. He wants to know if you ever go to the park."

"I live about ninety miles from Yellowstone. I go there every year."

A broad smile crossed Elmer's face.

"Have you ever seen bears?" Elmer asked.

"I've seen bears, moose, elk, deer, and mountain sheep. I photographed a bear with two cubs in Yellowstone last year. I could send you a photo if you like." Elmer nodded enthusiastically.

"I was telling Elmer that you collect stories about UFOs and write books about them. I asked him if he would be willing to share what he saw that night the spaceship collided with the coal train. Do you remember telling me the story, Elmer?"

Elmer nodded and hung his head.

"Don't worry," said Ethel. "She'll never tell your name or anyone else in this town that she met you. You can tell her everything, and she won't tell nobody you told her."

"Promise?" he said.

"I promise. If I ever write about your story, I will not reveal your name."

"Good," said Elmer. "I don't want my dad to know."

"I understand."

"I used to work in the mine. Started when I was twelve. My dad made me quit school in the 6th grade. He spent his whole life working in the mines; he expected I would do the same. When I was a boy, I used to watch the coal trains leaving on the tracks and wondered where they were going. I wanted to hop one and go with them, but I was stuck working in the mines, not going anywhere."

"How did you happen to see the UFO?"

"I was working that night. My shift ended, and I stopped off at the truck stop for breakfast. I did that every night. Eat my breakfast before going home and to bed. Lots of the guys did that."

"How old were you?" I asked.

"Fourteen or maybe fifteen."

"Were you driving at that age?"

"I been driving since I was eight," he said as if surprised by my question.

"Did you see the UFO after you got off work?"

"No. It was after I had breakfast. I generally headed home

around 3 a.m. Same time as my buddies. I got in my truck and headed for home. It was a dark night. Cloudy. No moon. About four miles from the truck stop, I turned off on the road to our place. About a half mile down the road, I saw a light in the woods. I thought it was strange and figured somebody might be in trouble. I took a right turn and headed toward the light. As I got closer, I had trouble figuring out what was going on. The lights were so bright, I couldn't make out anything. Then, the worst thing happened. My truck engine kept cutting out. I decided to park and walk the rest of the way."

"How far were you from the light at this time?"

"Maybe two hundred feet."

"I put my flashlight in my pocket, got my shotgun, and headed in the direction of the light."

"Your shotgun?"

"I wasn't about to go there unarmed. I didn't know what I was dealing with. I always have my shotgun with me. It's legal."

"When did you decide you were seeing a UFO?"

"When I entered the woods, I crept along the outskirts of the light. I wanted to make sure I knew what was going on before identifying myself. That's when I saw a silver spaceship parked in a clearing beyond the woods. I saw four, sometimes five, men milling around a gaping hole in the side of the ship. I watched as they patched it. It was amazing. They brought this thin sheet of matching colored material and placed it on the hole and it clung to the side like it was part of it. After they completed the chore, others appeared and inspected it. It was about that time that I saw flashlights in the distance and heard voices. I jumped up and yelled at them that someone was coming. They looked in my direction and immediately disappeared inside the machine and the next thing I know, the spaceship began to spin. It came straight toward me and hovered over me. I heard these strange voices in my head. I heard someone say, 'We're your friend. Thank you for watching over us. You helped us and now we will help you.' Suddenly a bolt of light came out of the ship, and it struck me. I felt like my brain was electrified."

"What happened when the people carrying flashlights appeared?"

"There were about ten of them. Some were dressed in uniforms. I stayed hidden. I didn't want to go to jail. They walked around and around. There was one man with a machine that he pointed at the ground and another who took some of the dirt and put it in a plastic bag. Another man was taking photos. That didn't make much sense to me, but he even took a photo of a broken limb."

"Do you think they saw the spacecraft fly away?" I asked.

"I don't think so. When it took off, it was silent. There were no lights. I could see it because the moon had finally come out, and as it went upward, I could see its shape against the sky."

"How big was the craft?"

"I'm not very good at sizes." He looked around the room. "It was about six times as big around and twice as high as this room."

"That would make it about sixty feet around and eighteen feet high."

He shrugged his shoulders and smiled.

"Did you get a good look at the men?"

"I couldn't make out anything about them other than they were dressed in silver jumpsuits, like racecar drivers wear. I couldn't make out their faces. They had a shimmering, silver glow about them. I call them the shining silver men. That's how I think of them."

"Did they wear helmets?"

"No helmets. They were kind of small. Probably no taller than Ethel."

"I'm five feet," Ethel announced.

"How big was the hole in the side of the craft?" I asked.

"About the size of this table. I never knew anything existed that could repair a hole like that, then take off, and fly away. That's a miracle. I bet the boys at the racetrack would sure like to have that kind of metal. Just repair their cars on the spot."

"Anything else you can tell me about that night."

"One thing, when it took off, it didn't make any sound. I thought that was strange, and it didn't smell like airplane fuel. It smelled funny. I wonder what they used for gasoline."

"When did you realize that you probably were witnessing the repair of a UFO?"

"Well, I think I knew it all along. The repair was the big thing. The next day, I heard at the mines about the coal train that collided with a spacecraft. They said the government guys said it was national security and no one should talk about it, but that next morning it was in the paper. That's when I knew for sure. I came over the next morning and told Ethel. It was exciting to think that I was watching aliens. I always wanted to see aliens. I knew about them from comic books. I wish I'd gone over and said hello. Maybe they would've taken me for a ride."

"Can you tell me if seeing the UFO changed your life in anyway?" I asked.

"You must swear you will never say a word. You, too, Ethel. You got to swear, too."

After we both agreed to keep Elmer's revelation a secret, he finished his apple pie and looked directly at me, but it was a different Elmer. He was no longer the shy, reticent man I had originally met, but a confident, alert, man with a very different demeanor and facial expression.

"I used to be dumb," Elmer began. "But I'm not anymore, but I don't tell anyone. I'm much smarter now. The aliens made me smarter."

"I don't understand what you are telling me."

"When the UFO left, it came directly over me and paused. I heard a voice in my head that I no longer had to work in the coal mines, but I could do anything I wanted to do. At first, I didn't believe it, but I began to notice that I could read things I could never read before. I started going to the library and reading. I bought a Kindle and started reading all the latest fiction novels and then I moved to non-fiction. I read all the masters of fiction. Now, I'm writing my own series. I publish on Amazon. I make enough money doing that I no longer work in the coal mines. I pick up odd jobs so no one will catch on to what happened to me. I'm a new man. All because of the aliens. So, yes, they impacted my life in a major way. They gave me a life."

After Elmer finished his story, we drank coffee and Elmer ate another piece of apple pie and ice cream and talked about bears and Yellowstone.

Ethel was right. Elmer was not dumb, but the source of his intelligence was not what she expected, nor I. The most amazing thing about him was he could morph back and forth between the "dumb Elmer" and the post-UFO Elmer. I spent two days with Elmer and saw him greet townspeople in the manner they expected; but when we were alone, it was obvious that something miraculous had happened to him. Ethel is still trying to comprehend it. Despite his new intelligence, his interest in bears and Yellowstone never wavered. I promised if he came to Montana, I would personally take him to Yellowstone. In the meantime, I made a copy of two photos I had taken in Yellowstone, framed them, and mailed them off to Elmer along with James Halfpenny's book, Yellowstone Bears in the Wild. I also included signed copies of my own books. A week later, I got an email from Elmer announcing that he had now joined the space age, owned a computer and had an email address. He thanked me for my letter and gift. He said it was the first present he had ever received and that he had saved the box because it came all the way from Montana. He is currently making plans to visit Montana.

4. ARLIS' STORY: STAR TRAVELER, THE SUPER DOG

Arlis lives alone in a cabin by the river on the outskirts of an Alaskan village. A twenty-eight-year-old veteran of Afghanistan, he lived a subsistence lifestyle. Most of his life centered on the thirty sled dogs he kept in his backyard. I met him at a local dog race held each year as a preliminary trial for the sled dog teams that entered regional and statewide competitions. Arlis' team won that day. Later that evening at a community potlatch, I heard him say that each of his sled dogs was named for stars and constellations. I approached him to offer my congratulations and ask him about his choice of names for his dogs. When I discovered that he had spent time in Montana, we had an instant connection. When he offered to take me dog sledding, I took him up on his invitation. While I expected to experience a new adventure, I soon learned that there was much more to Arlis than dog racing.

When I drove into Arlis' driveway, he waved to me but continued feeding his sled dogs. I got out of the car, and the dogs barked and jumped as I walked toward their kennels. I watched as he lovingly acknowledged each dog and gave it individual attention. He was a tall man, and bundled in his snowsuit and mukluks he looked like a man who could have played defensive end on any NFL team. Despite his size, there was a softer side to the man, whose long hair curled around his ears beneath his knit cap. He had a smile that could light up a room, and despite his reputation for bravery in Afghanistan, he was a gentle man with an unassuming manner.

"They get excited when someone comes around. Probably because we don't have too many visitors," he said, as he placed the last bowl in front of his lead dog, Cassiopeia. "Come, I'll show you around the place." He held my arm as we walked the slippery path around his cabin, pointing out the different structures and his plans for expansion.

"How long have you lived here?" I asked.

"Six years. I went to the military right out of high school. Ended up in Afghanistan. Soon as my enlistment was up, I headed for Alaska."

"Is this your first experience with sled dogs?"

"I had sled dogs growing up, but I wanted a place where I could breed and race dogs. Land is more expensive in the lower forty-eight. Alaska seemed like the perfect place. My uncle invested some money, and with what I'd saved while I was in Afghanistan, I bought two hundred acres of land. Besides, after the war, I didn't much like being around people. I liked being alone."

"Well, you're certainly alone out here," I said. He looked at me and smiled but did not respond.

"Come, let's have some coffee and talk before I take you on that sled dog ride I promised," he said. I followed him up the slippery stairs to the doorway. His one-room cabin was filled with homemade furniture. A poster of Elvis hung on the wall. "My uncle gave me that poster," he said. "He met Elvis years ago at a concert in Rapid City. His last one I guess."

"You told me that you named your dogs after stars and constellations. Could you tell me about that?"

"Planets, too," he said, as he poured two cups of coffee. "I have Mars, Venus, Saturn, and Pluto in the backyard," he said, smiling. "I like to watch the stars and planets at night." He pointed to a small telescope positioned in front of one of the two windows in the cabin.

"When did you get interested in astronomy?" I asked.

"The first time the Star Men came," he said. He looked at me awkwardly. "Look, I know you think you came here because I promised to take you dog sledding, but I had another motive." I watched him pace the floor in front of the kitchen table. "I know you write books about UFOs. My uncle brought me your book last summer." He walked to his bookshelf and pulled out a copy of my first book. "I was stunned when I met you at the potlatch. I had no idea you worked with the local school. I was afraid to say anything at the dog races. I didn't want people to know about my visitors. I took a chance inviting you for dog sledding. I don't know what I would've done if you had refused my invitation."

"Are you telling me that you have had an encounter with the Star People?" I asked.

"It was the first winter after I built my cabin. The river freezes over every winter. By January, the ice is two to three feet deep. One night I stayed up later than usual reading." He paused and took a sip of his coffee.

"Did you see a UFO that night?" I asked.

"I no sooner turned off the lights, when the whole cabin was lit up. It looked like daylight outside. I pulled on my pants and boots, grabbed my coat and rifle, and rushed outside. That's when I saw a UFO with a circle of white lights outlining it, just hanging in the sky about twenty feet over the river. After a few seconds, it slowly descended and rested on the river. I stood there in amazement. I was afraid to move or do anything."

"What were your dogs doing?" I asked.

"Nothing. Cassiopeia stood on her kennel as if in a trance."

"How long did you stand there?"

"Long enough to feel the cold seeping into my bones. I ran back into the house, stood in front of the stove, and put on my snow suit and headed outside again." He paused and took another sip of his coffee. "By the time I got outside, I saw some activity around the ship. There were people there, or what looked like people, outside the ship, standing on the ice. They seemed to be checking something along one side. It was difficult to see what was going on because the lights were so bright. But there was one thing I found strange. They weren't walking on the ice. They were skimming it."

"Skimming? I don't understand."

"You know. Skimming. Like their feet weren't touching the ice. They kind of floated over the ice."

"Did they know you were watching them?"

"Not at first. Then Cassiopeia started barking, and they looked toward the kennels. That's when they saw me. As one of them broke from the group—there were four of them—I pointed my rifle at him and ordered him to stop. He kept coming and telling me they were friends. That I didn't have to fear them."

"How did you respond to that?" I asked.

"I dropped my rifle. I don't know why. It just seemed to be the right thing, but I stood my ground as he zoomed up the bank."

"Sorry for interrupting, but what do you mean when you say he zoomed up the bank?"

"It was like he flew up the bank. He was airborne. It was the darnedest thing I'd ever seen. I forgot I might be in danger. I was so amazed that he was flying."

"When he approached you, what did you do?"

"I backed up a little ways, and he repeated that he meant me no harm."

"Did you feel he was friendly?"

"Not particularly. I didn't know who he was, and out in these parts you don't trust strangers. I asked him if he was with the government and where he came from. He pointed to the stars and said far away."

"Is that when you realized you were dealing with Star People?" I asked.

"I was still skeptical. I mean, I live forty miles from town. My closest neighbor is ten miles away. I don't have a telephone and cells don't work out here. If something happened, I'm on my own. I was still thinking they were military. We have bases in Alaska, and I thought it might be an experimental craft and he was just covering up."

"So what did you do?"

"I told him to prove it."

Arlis picked up his cup, carried it to the stove, and refilled it.

He offered to refill mine before continuing the story. "Then he picked me up and flew me inside the craft. He took me to an area on the top deck that must have been the control center. There were all kinds of screens that looked like computers. There were two other beings inside the control center."

"Can you describe the area you call the control center?"

"There were screens built into a panel. Something like Star Trek but not exactly. There were two beings sitting in front of the screens. One seemed to be monitoring what was going on outside. The other one seemed to be a map of the sky. Another showed a view of the area around the cabin. In the center of the room was a clear tower. I saw no levers or means of flying the craft."

"Can you describe the tower?"

"It looked like glass, but I'm sure it wasn't. I touched it and it wasn't glass but some kind of strange plastic that melded to my hand. I pulled it back and it went back to its original form. I tried again and the same thing happened. My handprint was firmly imbedded in the material, but then it re-formed to its original shape. They told me it was a pliable material that could withstand any shock. It was about as big around as a number three washtub. It came up out of the floor and ran all the way to the ceiling. He said it was the power system for their ship."

"Did you ask him how he powered the ship?"

"I asked him about fuel, and he said they got power from the atmosphere to recharge their system so they never had to use fuel as we know it. I told him I would like to have that system if it powered lights, but he didn't answer."

"What were the beings doing in front of the screens?"

"Sitting like they were machines. They didn't acknowledge me or talk to me. I think my guide was the only living being on the ship. I think those two and the three others outside were robots."

"You called the visitor a living being. Why do you think that?"

"Because the others looked like machines. He was the only one who looked like a living, breathing creature."

"Maybe I should ask my question another way. Are you calling him human because he appeared as a biological entity—by that I mean, did he resemble a human?"

"He had two arms, a head, a middle, and two legs. But there was one thing. He had inhuman strength. He lifted me up and flew me into the spaceship. I was stunned by his power. I didn't try to resist because it would have been useless."

"Did he show you anything else?"

"He took me to the lower level and showed me his living space. There was a type of hammock inside, but it wasn't like an ordinary hammock. It was suspended in the air like a hammock, but it was more like a web of silky strands. There were machines in the room, which he indicated were used for nutrition and sleep. There was no desk or books or anything personal."

"Did you see anything else?"

"A storage area where they keep things alive."

"What did they keep alive?"

"I only saw plants in glass containers. After that, he asked me if I was convinced that he came from the stars. I had to admit it was likely. I invited him to visit my home, but he declined. He said he had a schedule to keep. Then he asked me about other people. He said they didn't visit areas with people if it could be avoided. They believed my cabin to be abandoned or they would not have chosen this site. I told him no one would see them on my land. They would be safe. He said he would see me again. Then the next thing I know, I'm standing on the bank, watching the ship lift off the ice and go straight upward until it suddenly disappeared."

"Did you learn anything else?"

"I asked him if the others were robots. He said they were not really robots but crossbreeds of biological parts and mechanical parts. He called them Synthetics. He said the crossbreeds were the best companions in space because they work in any atmosphere and feel no danger. They do not need to sleep or eat. They maintain and pilot the spaceship."

"Did they appear as robots we might be familiar with?"

"No. They looked more human. Their skin looked like stretched rubber. There were no lines on their faces like they were wearing a mask."

"And the Star Man, what did he look like?"

"More human. He was dark skinned like me. He had round eyes that were larger than human eyes. I never saw his hair. He had a covering over his head that was a part of his suit. He was probably six foot three or four. I'm six foot two and he was slightly taller than me. There were instruments attached to his arms around his wrists. I asked him if the instruments were weapons, and he said that he never carried weapons. He had no need for weapons."

"Have you been visited since that encounter?"

"Three times. They always come in the winter. They land on the ice and four beings come out. Three are the robot kind and then my friend. On his second visit, he came into my cabin. He was fascinated by my book collection. He picked up an axe and asked me how I used it. He was interested in a plane that I used to shave logs. He put his finger in sugar bowl and tasted the sugar. He tasted the salt, too."

"Did he show any emotions?"

"None that I remember. I kept wondering if he understood what I was telling him."

"How did he react to the sugar and salt?"

"There was no reaction at all. He showed no pleasure or displeasure, but he asked me for a sample."

"How did you communicate with him?"

"We never talked. We just understood one another. I always knew what he was thinking."

"Anything else you learned?"

"There is one thing that happened that was remarkable."

"Please tell me about it."

"On the second visit when he came into the cabin, he saw a small pup I was caring for. The pup couldn't walk. I brought him inside and hoped that with the warmth of the stove and massage I could help him. But the pup had not been responsive, and I feared I would have to put him down. When the star man saw him, I told him the problem. He picked the pup up and asked me if he could take him. A year later, he returned the pup. He was now strong and healthy. He is one of the best dogs I have for his age. I will introduce you to him before you leave. He's a super-dog. I call him Star Traveler. He's probably the only sled dog on Earth that has traveled to other worlds."

"That's an interesting story."

"I don't know what they did, but I'm telling you, there was nothing I could do to save him. The Star Man has great powers. He healed him and made him stronger than his brothers and sisters. He's the smartest dog I have ever seen. He seems to understand every word I speak to him. But there was another difference. If you part his hair near the base of his skull, there is a long thin scar. I think they must have operated on his brain. I will show you when we go outside. I'm grooming him to replace Cassiopeia."

"Are there any other things you learned from the Star Man?"

"He told me their planet was covered with snow and ice and that the people live in underground cities. I asked if the snow melted, but he said it was covered with ice and snow year-round. There was no sun like the one we have, but they have created artificial suns underground. At one time, there was a sun, but it burned out and their world went cold. So that's when they moved underground."

"Did he tell you anything about their families, population, and their belief in God?"

"He saw my crucifix on the wall above my bed. He wanted to know about it. I explained in simple terms the story of God and Jesus. He seemed interested but said they did not know God or Jesus in his world. I showed him my Bible but he didn't understand how it could be the word of God."

"Can you think of anything else?"

"No. If I do, I can write you about it. But he doesn't stay long when he comes. An hour maybe less. He doesn't like to stay long. They do their maintenance and leave. He said he wasn't supposed to interact with humans, but that he knew I wouldn't tell anyone because no one would believe me."

"Do you think he will come again?"

"I expect him anytime. His visits have always been in January. I might have missed him since I was away for the race. But there are still a few days in the month."

Later that morning, Arlis loaded me into the sled along with various survival items. We rode through forests and ended up along the river below his cabin. The dogs were amazing, as they seemed to be an extension of the man who led them. We paused in a clearing to drink a cup of coffee from a thermos bottle. Arlis explained to me the plans he had for the future. When I asked him if his repeated visitations by the Star Man had influenced his life in any way, he took a moment to respond.

"I never thought much about life beyond this planet. In our way, we always pray for all the four leggeds, the two leggeds, and the winged creatures. So it is not that I believed in aliens or Star People, it is just that our prayers appear to include every living creature in the universe. So it doesn't bother me religiously. I don't believe that God only created man."

He put the cup back on the thermos and stowed it in the sled.

"Do you think the Star Man has any evil purpose in mind?"

"I don't think my friend means any harm to the Earth. I believe he's nothing more than an explorer such as our astronauts. The only thing that bothers me is his secrecy. I ask myself repeatedly why he's unwilling to reveal himself to the world. If he can travel throughout the universe, why not share his knowledge. But then when I think of how his knowledge might be used, I understand."

"I'm really interested in why you call him a friend. Can you explain?"

"I call him a friend because any man or being who cares enough to save a dog is my friend."

I have seen Arlis twice since our first visit. His Star Man continues to visit him every year in January. Star Traveler is now the proud father of six new puppies, who seem to possess the strength and intelligence of their father. I think of Arlis on cold sub-zero nights in Montana and wonder about the Star Man who lives in a world of ice. I find myself agreeing with Arlis: any being that heals a dog is a friend in my opinion.

5. THEODORE'S STORY: THEY MAY BE GODS

Theodore went into the uranium mines when he was eighteen and worked there alongside his brothers and cousins for twenty years. When his health began to affect his performance, his employer let him go without a pension. He told me the uranium mines were a hotbed of UFO activity and that sometimes the craft landed. This is the story of what happened one night as he was leaving the mines.

I met Theodore at his home near Albuquerque, New Mexico. When I arrived at his home with two boxes of food, tears welled up in his eyes. He reached out and unexpectedly embraced me. When I opened my handbag and pulled out two boxes of Twinkies, which the grocery store clerk told me was his favorite treat, his face lit up like a Christmas tree.

"Thank you for inviting me into your home," I said as I sat down in a chair at a small table. "I'm honored to meet you."

"I'm honored, daughter. Thank you for your generosity. We will include you in our prayers." He opened a small box on the table and brought out a medallion. It was made of in-laid mother of pearl, jasper, and turquoise. "This is for you," he said.

"Please, your company and your story are all I need. I'm the one who is thankful."

He reached out and opened my hand. "I made it for you. If you look closely, you will see that it is from the Star People's perspective looking down on earth. I saw this view in a dream and I knew that you would treasure this more than anyone else."

I looked at the man who sat across from me. At thirty-eight, it was clear that his years in the mines had aged him. He had a stooped appearance but did not look like a man who suffered from lung cancer. His calloused hands were swollen, but he appeared healthy.

"You mentioned to me that you had an encounter with a UFO a few months ago," I began. "Would it be possible for you to tell me about it?"

"I'd be happy to tell you. I'm not the only one who saw it, but I may be the only one who talked to the Star Men."

"Please start at the beginning."

"Many times, when I left the mines, I'd saw the silver ships soaring above the edge of the sky. Some people say the star travelers take uranium. That they need it in their ships. But I don't think so. They monitor what we do because they have underground bases near the mines."

"How do you know that?" I asked.

"They told me. They took me there." He got up and stoked the small pot-belly wood stove in the corner and added more wood. Smoke from the stove came out into the room and stung my eyes and nose. "Sorry, the stove has seen its better days," he commented as he sat down again.

"When did you first see the Star Men?" I asked.

"I've been seeing them for years. They are a common sight in this part of the country, but it was my last day on the job that I talked with them."

"Could you tell me about that?" I asked.

"I worked the four to midnight shift for twenty years. It was the shift that nobody wanted, but for me it was good. I got home and went to bed and had breakfast with my wife and kids the next morning. In twenty years, I never missed a day of work. When I got sick, the company let me go. My wife and I survive on gifts from friends like you and whatever our son can give us. I'm sorry. I got off track. You came to hear about my encounter with the Star Men, not my sad life."

I could tell the loss of his job had taken an immense toll on his life. "I want you to take your time and tell your story as you feel comfortable. I am in no hurry. So don't apologize."

He paused as his wife, Mabel, appeared with a pot of tea and delivered two Twinkies on a plate and paper towels, one for each of us. "That night, my last night, I was low. A man is his job in many ways. You get up every day, you go to work, and you repeat it every day, and at the end of the month you get paid. On that night, I was told not to return to work the next day. It was hard for me. So instead of going home and telling Mabel, I drove out into the desert. There had been a lot of UFO activity the past month, and it was interesting to go out in the desert and watch the night sky."

"Did you see UFOs that night?"

"As I drove out of the parking lot, I saw two UFOs in the sky, but they were far away. I thought nothing of it at the time."

"So when did you make contact with the Star People?" I asked.

"I drove about twenty miles into the desert. I parked my pickup on an overhanging ledge. The sky was black, but star-filled. Then all of a sudden, like a lightning flash in the night, I saw a UFO larger than our little village come into view. It was quiet as a cat stalking a mouse. I got out of my truck and stood on the ledge and watched. Suddenly, I felt myself soaring upward toward the craft. I thought I must be dreaming. It was impossible for man to fly, and yet I looked at my pickup below and knew I was flying."

"What did you think about that?"

"I wasn't afraid. I knew all about the Star Men. They came to us in the ancient times and they still come. There were three who appeared to a woman and her daughters not too far from here last year. After it happened they went to the tribal chairman and told him their story. It was decided it was a sacred event. A celebration and prayer were held. UFOs and Star Men are real. We see them all the time."

"Did they take you onboard their craft?" I asked.

"I was taken aboard and placed in a cubicle of blue light for a few minutes, then the door to the cubicle opened and I walked out and was greeted by tall, white men. They also had smaller men who stood in the shadows and followed us. I asked them if they were going to kill me, and they said they were going to save me."

"How did they speak to you?" I asked.

"I could hear their voices in my head loud and clear. There were times I did not understand their words, but they always spoke in my native language so I would know what they meant. Sometimes they would use English words if there was no such word in my language."

"Are you telling me they spoke your Native language?"

"Yes. They knew our language. They spoke it perfectly."

"Did they tell you the results of their examination?"

"They said I had uranium poisoning with cancer throughout my body and that they could heal me, but it would take more than one treatment. They asked for my permission. Of course, I agreed."

"What kind of treatment?"

"They took me into another room, removed my clothing, put me into another cubicle, and ran a blue light over me. Then they took me out and wrapped me in a fabric-like gauze and immersed me in a tub of something that looked like blue jello. They made me stay there for what seemed like an hour. The gel was very soothing, and I could feel my body burning inside, but my skin was cool. It was the strangest feeling I have ever had."

"What did they do with you once they removed you from the tub of gel?"

"They returned me to the cubicle and ran the blue light over me. After that, they placed me in the chair again and examined me. They took blood and skin samples again. They placed a metal instrument over my head and left. Later they returned and said the treatment had been effective, but we would have to do it again. It would take time for me to heal."

"What happened next?"

"They returned me to my pickup and told me to return in one week at the same time."

"Did you do that?"

"I've met with the Star Men six weeks at the same time and same place. I'm almost healed. Can you believe it? I was a dying man and now I am regaining my health and I feel good."

"What have you learned from your experience?" I asked.

"I've learned so many things. For one thing, they monitor the mine and similar mines worldwide. I've learned they do not eat solid food. I've learned that they have gardens, but not for food, but to protect the plant life of the planet. They do not eat food but have a method of feeding their bodies through energy. They also use energy to induce sleep. I don't understand this at all."

"Do you believe them to be human like you and me?"

"No. They may be gods. I'm not sure. But they told me they replaced parts of their body with parts that never die and never disease. Their outward appearance is that of a human, but they're not human. Their medicine became very advanced over the years, but instead of fighting diseases, they devised a way to prevent the body from becoming diseased by substituting parts. All life is now created in a laboratory. I guess they are machines with human skin and hair."

"But they do have medicine to cure you."

"Yes. They said they had conquered all diseases, but it was easier to build a body than to cure it. They said in many ways man can heal himself by just using his own brain power and energy. I have seen them use their own energy to heal others."

"Others? Are you saying they abduct others?"

"Yes. They told me they are selective in the humans they heal."

"Do they observe humans?"

"All the time."

"Does that concern you?"

"I believe God watches everything we do. So no, it doesn't bother me."

"How many more treatments do you have?"

"One more and it will be over."

"Why did they choose you?"

"Because they said I have something I'm supposed to do."

"What is that?"

"I don't know. Maybe it is to talk to you. Maybe they want the world to know about them through you. I can think of nothing else."

I have seen Theodore twice since I first met him. He is healthy and strong. He has been unable to find employment, so he spends his time gardening and creating jewelry, which he sells at the local fairs. At best, it provides him with a subsistence living. Last year after my first visit, I anonymously ordered a new stove to be delivered and installed at his home by a local businessman who runs a nonprofit that purchases stoves for the elderly and those in need on the reservation. When I made my visit the following year, a bright red wood stove graced his small home. He was very proud of it and told me that someone was definitely looking out for him. I was happy that I was that someone.

6. COY'S STORY:
THEY STOLE TWO BUFFALO

Coy described himself as an Indian cowboy. He managed the tribal ranch and its buffalo herd. Described by his men as a hands-on leader, he was more likely to be seen on a horse riding the fence line than sitting behind a desk. I met Coy at the tribal office one day. He invited me to come out to the ranch if I ever had time and he would show me the operation. One day I decided to take him up on his offer. Following a business trip to meet with the school superintendent, I called the ranch and asked Coy if a Friday night visit would be convenient. For the next two days, I was his guest in the manager's house and rode the fence lines and photographed the buffalo herd. On the last day of my visit, he organized a family barbecue and invited the wives and children of his wranglers to the house. After a chuck wagon dinner, the families gathered for story time. One of the wranglers told the story of a ghost owl that visited the ranch. Another told a story of a brave who defeated an enemy raiding party with a magical bow. The oldest cowboy of the group told the story of his grandfather who once met General Custer and predicted he would die in a great battle. As the stories went full circle, one young cowboy told of a sighting of a UFO when he was seven. As his story ended, Coy's wife, Aubrey, leaned over and told him he should tell his UFO story. But he shook his head, and when it came his turn, he told the story of a white woman who haunted Bridger Creek. The next morning, I asked Coy if he would tell me his UFO story.

"There isn't a lot to tell, but then, I guess you can be the judge," he began as his wife served the two of us bacon and scrambled eggs. "I told Aubrey about it, but I haven't told the others, although they probably wonder why I added two men on night patrol. I told them that we'd heard of rustlers in the area and wanted to protect the herd. They seemed to accept the explanation."

I watched Coy as he drank his coffee. He was a small man, standing no more than five foot six in his cowboy boots. A tick over his left eye made it appear as though he was winking, and when it occurred, he self-consciously looked away. The scars on his rough hands revealed a man who had worked hard all of his life.

"Do you mind if I tape your story?" I asked.

He watched as I pushed the button on the tape recorder, then began: "We have electric fences all around the ranch. It's the only way to safely contain buffalo. There is a control panel in the basement, which alerts me to any problems with the fence. It was about 6 p.m. when the alarm sounded. It was getting dark, and I didn't want to bother the guys. I knew the location and it was accessible by vehicle, so I decided to drive out and see if I could take care of the problem. It was about a twenty-minute drive."

"Was anyone on patrol that night?"

"No. I set up the night patrols after this incident."

"Did you find the problem?"

"I did, and after several attempts to repair the problem, I decided I'd have to get Willard on the job. He's our electrician and keeps the fence up and working. I called his cabin and told him where I was and that I was unable to fix the problem. He agreed to be there within a half hour."

"Did you stay at the site?"

"I did. I thought I should wait in case he needed help. I had a book in the pickup and decided to read while I waited. I reached up to turn on the overhead light and it didn't work. I tried to start my pickup and it wouldn't start. I got out, opened the hood, but couldn't find anything wrong. I closed the hood, climbed back in the pickup, and turned the key in the ignition, but nothing happened."

"But you saw nothing else?"

"Not right away. But about five minutes later, I saw six bright lights headed toward me. I thought it was car lights, even though

I thought the formation was strange. They looked like headlights from the distance."

He paused as Aubrey placed a plate of toast on the table and then joined us. Coy picked up two slices, made a bacon and egg sandwich, and took a bite.

"I sat there for a few minutes watching the lights and trying to figure out what they were doing. When they were about three hundred yards from me, they were no longer coming toward me, but they veered off toward a small group of hills. That's when the six lights became two. They just merged into two. It was the strangest thing I'd ever seen."

"Did you have any idea what they were doing?"

"Well, I soon found out. I got out of my truck for a better look, when all of a sudden part of the buffalo herd came stampeding around the base of the hill and ran toward the center of the meadow below me. I knew the lights had frightened them, and knowing that the electric fence was not electrified, I climbed back in the pickup in case they decided to run right through it. I knew it was a dangerous situation, but there was nothing I could do about it. The pickup was dead."

He paused, took another bite of his sandwich, and took a sip of his coffee.

"As you were sitting there, were the lights still in view?"

"The lights just hung there in the sky above the hills. Then suddenly, they moved forward and down. The buffalo began running again and the lights kept coming closer and closer. Then suddenly, it was like they dropped out of the sky and came to rest on the floor of the meadow. I looked at the buffalo herd and they were suddenly calm and not moving. I saw faint lights at the bottom of two circular crafts. I knew they were not American. We didn't have anything like that. I'm a vet and I know we had nothing like that."

"What did you do?"

"At first, I sat and waited. Then I saw doorways open on each craft and a human figure came out of each one. I reached for my shotgun and loaded it. I got my flashlight out of the glove compartment and slipped out of the pickup. I checked the fence. It was still not electrified. I climbed over it and quietly headed for the craft. When I got close enough, I called out to them. They whirled around and leaped toward the spacecraft. I aimed my shotgun near their feet and shot. After two shots, my gun jammed, but I yelled at them to get off the ranch. They never turned toward me. Instead, they grabbed a buffalo and leaped into the craft, and it immediately went upward. Straight up. Never seen a thing like that in my life. They went directly east, and then all of a sudden they were gone and so were two of our buffalo."

"What do you mean when you say they leaped into the craft?"

"They leaped into the air, maybe ten feet, landing directly into the doorway of the craft."

"How did they get out of the craft to begin with?"

"You aren't going to believe this, but they floated to the ground."

"And you said, there were two buffalo missing. Is that correct?"

"They took them. When I shot at them, each one picked up a buffalo and carried it away?"

"How could they do that? Don't buffalo weigh a lot?"

"A male can weigh as much as two thousand pounds, but that didn't seem to bother them. They picked them up in one arm and leaped into their crafts. Definitely not something any human could do."

"Did they ever return them?"

"Not alive. We found two carcasses two days later. They had died from surgery, it appeared. The strangest thing, they were mostly intact minus their innards, eyes, and feet. We took the carcasses to the university vet school. They dissected them but had no explanation about the surgery. The dead buffalo looked like someone who operated on them had the skills of a vet but probably advanced tools unknown to our veterinarians."

"Can you remember anything else about the scene?" I asked.

"The other buffalo stayed clear of the carcasses. I never even saw an insect on them. Generally, when we harvest buffalo, we leave the skulls outside where ants and other insects can clean them off. It is very difficult to clean a buffalo skull so the best way is to leave it out for the ants, and after they've done their job, we wash and clean it with peroxide. But no insect ever came near these buffalo."

"What happened to the buffalo carcasses?"

"We brought them back to the ranch. I had the men dig a grave and bury them far away from the grazing area. I don't know if the carcasses were contaminated, but I didn't want to take any chances. Some of the men grumbled about my decision. They wanted to salvage the meat, but I didn't want to take any chances."

"I have another question: Did Willard ever show up?"

"I made it back to my pickup and was sitting in the cab trying to make sense out of what I had seen. I was trying to figure out what was wrong with my shotgun. It had never jammed before. I popped out the shell and was looking down the barrel when Willard drove up. He took one look at me and said that he hoped I wasn't aiming at him. We both laughed. Then Willard tested the fence controls and said he couldn't find anything wrong. I was beginning to think I was crazy. I turned the key in the ignition and the pickup started. I apologized for getting Willard out of bed and followed him back to the ranch house."

He paused and finished his sandwich. Aubrey refilled our coffee cups.

"Can you describe the men you saw?"

"There wasn't enough light to make out any features. They wore light, reflective suits, and it looked like they might have been one piece. They also had headgear. I know they were afraid of my shotgun. And they could fly and jump like no normal human. And their strength. It was mind-boggling. How could anyone pick up a full-grown buffalo? I can't imagine such power. That's about all I can say about them."

"Anything else?"

"I think they were the ones who messed up the electricity. I think they shut off the electric fence, and I think they interfered with my pickup's engine. I don't think they did it on purpose, but I think it was a result of whatever they have on their ships. I'm sure they weren't expecting me, and when I shot at them, they bounded away. I mean they must have jumped ten feet to get back in their ship. That was quite a sight to see. I think the coach at the high school would like to have those kinds of jumpers on his track team."

"Has your encounter changed your life in anyway?" I asked.

"I guess there are several things. I spent the next day after the incident checking the fence alarm system. I bought cell phones for all my wranglers so they can keep in touch with the office should anything out of the ordinary happen. I no longer feel that we're in control. If they have the ability to upset our electrical system and prevent vehicles from running, it makes us vulnerable to them. We wouldn't stand a chance if they decided to invade. But they only seemed to be interested in the buffalo. Why would they mutilate the buffalo? It certainly was not for the meat."

"I can tell you, I have heard of a similar event."

"I figured as much."

He drank his coffee, told me goodbye, and invited me back to the ranch anytime. I watched him put on his cowboy hat and stride toward the door. Aubrey walked to the door and gave him a kiss. He returned it and looked back at me. "Come anytime. Maybe we can go hunt the UFOs. I'll let you know if they come back."

He paused in the doorway and looked at me. "There is one other thing. I worry more now. I used to think this was the safest place in the world, but now I don't know. I just hope it doesn't happen again. I don't like to worry."

I have taken Coy and Aubrey up on their invitation and have visited them twice since he told me his story. I love riding the range with Coy. There is nothing like heading out at dawn and watching a buffalo herd graze in the morning light. There have been no more sightings of UFOs at the ranch. Perhaps Coy was right: the aliens do not like guns.

7. SHAWNEE'S STORY: THEY HIJACKED MY CAR

I was visiting relatives on the reservation one weekend when a woman approached me in the community grocery store and told me she had read my book Encounters with Star People, and that she had a story to tell that even her family did not believe. She asked if I had the time to listen to her story. I told her I always had the time to listen, and we agreed to meet at her house at noon. This is Shawnee's story.

I arrived at Shawnee's house a few minutes before noon. She welcomed me into her kitchen where she was busy making soup for her family's dinner. She cleared off a chair at her kitchen table and told me to sit, while she brought two cups of black coffee to the table.

"Thank you for talking with me. My family thinks I'm crazy and I must have dreamed these events, but I assure you I'm not crazy, and what I'm about to tell you is the honest-to-God's truth, and I have a witness, although she doesn't like to talk about it. She doesn't want to get involved."

She stood, walked to the stove, and stirred her soup. I watched as she added a mixture of vegetables to the pot. She could have been an attractive woman, but it was obvious that she paid little attention to her appearance. Her coal black hair hung down her back in tangles and appeared as though it hadn't been combed in days. One look at her hands revealed she was a nail biter and a smoker. She wore stained sweat pants with a t-shirt that hit below her waist, revealing her navel.

"There are many ancient legends about Star People among my people," Shawnee said as she sat down. "When I was a child, I loved those stories. There were legends about people coming down from the sky and taking men and women to the stars. There were stories of women having star children and returning to live among the people. So I don't think my encounter is that unusual considering aliens have been visiting us for centuries."

She jumped up and peered into her pot of soup.

"You can't imagine how happy I am to meet you. I just want someone to listen to me who has an open mind and will not think I've lost my mind."

She reached for a pack of cigarettes and a lighter on the table. I watched her light the cigarette and open the window by the table, blowing the smoke toward the window screen.

"I'm always interested in true encounters with Star People," I said. "I've been told many stories during my travels, but I have to admit you are the first person to contact me in a convenience store."

She laughed nervously and took another drag on her cigarette. "I always speak the truth, or at least I try to. You can rest assured that my story is the truth," she said.

I did not respond to her declaration but watched as she tightened the salt and pepper shakers on the table.

"I never thought much about UFOs," she began. "I'd heard stories about UFOs from friends, but I never thought much about them until one night two years ago. I wanted to tell my story to you because you've had experiences with UFOs. Perhaps you can tell me if you've heard anything like my story."

She fell silent as the lid on the soup pot began to dance. She got up and lowered the heat.

"How many UFO cases have you heard?" she asked.

"Hundreds. Do you mind if I tape your story?" I asked, placing a small recorder on the table between us.

"No, but don't use my real name. I don't want a bunch of people trying to find me and asking me questions. I just want to talk to you. I need to share with someone, and you seem to be the perfect person. Everyone on the rez speaks well of you. They say you can be trusted."

"Thank you. And I promise I will never reveal your name or your location."

"Good. My friend Dakota was with me. I can take you to meet her later. I asked her to come and meet you, but she's babysitting for her sister. Dakota and I go all the way back to first grade. We have been friends forever."

"Tell me, where did you and Dakota have your encounter?"

"Once a month, Dakota and I take a day and go to the city, which is about seventy miles away. We leave early so we can stop at McDonalds for breakfast. We shop all day, stop for lunch, then we shop some more. On one such day, we were driving home. We stayed longer than usual, and halfway home it got dark."

Suddenly she jumped up and stirred her pot of soup before continuing her story. "There is one spot on the road where there are a lot of hills and curves. I was driving, and Dakota was talking about her kids, when all of a sudden we topped a hill and there in the middle of the road was a UFO. There was a blue glow around the bottom. I remember that because it was so beautiful."

She paused and walked to the counter and returned with the coffee carafe. She refilled our cups before sitting down.

"What was your reaction?" I asked.

"I stopped immediately and put the car in reverse. Suddenly a blinding beam was directed at us. Dakota started to scream when the car engine died. She was sure we were going to be abducted, and she would never see her kids again. As we sat there defenseless, we saw a figure approaching us. It was a tall human-like shadow. He came up to my side of the car and opened the door. He told me he needed my car." She stood and walked to the stove and stirred her soup. "Now I know this sounds crazy, but that's what he said."

"Did you say he wanted your car?"

"Yes. He said it without any emotion. He hijacked my car."

"Did he speak verbally to you?"

"I don't know. All I know is that he wanted my car, and there was no way in hell I was going to give him my car."

"What did you do?"

"About the time he said that, Dakota jumped out of the car and ran down the highway. She must have tripped. I saw her fall. She was sprawled in the middle of the road. I crawled across the seat and jumped out of the car. I ran to her, but she was unconscious. The next thing I remember, I woke up inside an unfamiliar, cold prison. The walls were gray metal. We were lying on these cold metal tables. Dakota was still unconscious. I looked around for some water, but there was nothing in the room. I tried to wake her, but she didn't move."

"Did you see any other beings besides the man who came to your car door?"

"No, just the hijacker. He came into the room where we were being held and told me that I had nothing to worry about. He said they needed my car to transport some passengers to the city. When I demanded to know what passengers, he told me that they were taking some of his people to the city."

"Did he explain?"

"He told me that they occasionally come to Earth and some of his people live on earth. Some forever; others stay only a few months. It was very confusing for me. I felt my heart beating inside my chest, but at that moment I wanted to make sure that I gathered every bit of information I could."

"I told him I needed my car."

"How did he react to that?"

"He told me that they would return my car as soon as they dropped off the passengers."

"So if you were half way home on a seventy-mile drive, that would mean, you have to wait about two hours. Did the UFO remain on the highway all that time?"

"Oh no, we were hovering high above the Earth, waiting for the car to return."

"What about your friend?"

"That's another thing. She remained unconscious, and I asked him what they did to her. He told me it was mind control, and that they had tried to use it on me, but I was not cooperative, whatever that means. All I know is that I was fully aware of what was going on."

"Did he tell you anything else?"

"He said it was difficult for his people to live on Earth, but the longer they stayed the easier it became. When I asked him why it was difficult because they appeared human, he told me that they could take the forms of humans, but they were not like humans. That's when he told me it would be too difficult for me if I knew what he really looked like. I demanded to know, something I would soon regret."

"What do you mean?"

"He showed his real self to me."

"What did he look like?"

All of a sudden Shawnee stood and burst out into tears. "He was hideous. Half animal, half bug, is the best way I can describe him. He changed into this form that was the strangest thing I have ever seen."

She dropped back to the chair and reached for a paper towel and wiped her eyes. "I'm sorry, but he was right. I should not have asked to see his true self. He was tall, maybe eight or nine feet. The best way to describe him was that he looked like a big grasshopper, or maybe an ant. I know that is unbelievable. I kept thinking how could such a creature fly the universe."

"What do you mean?"

"This thing was a bug. When he saw that I was upset, he immediately changed to his human form. He told me I should not be afraid, that he would not harm me. He then offered to take me on a tour of his ship. He took me to an upper deck of sorts, and there I saw four more aliens sitting around controls like a computer screen, but they weren't computers. He explained that the screens simply kept track of the different bodies in the Universe and that they used their minds to travel."

"Did he show you anything else?"

"He returned me to the room where Dakota was sleeping. He

told me that the driver was on his way back from the city and that I would soon be home. He walked over to a wall in the room and pressed a button. Suddenly, a small beverage-like center opened up and he brought me a cup of liquid. He told me to drink it, and I would forget all of this happened. I stared at the thick mucus like substance and told him I wanted to remember. Now I think I should have drunk it."

"Why do you think that?" I asked.

"Because it would be easier to be like Dakota. She remembers seeing the UFO but nothing else. She doesn't have nightmares, and she thinks nothing happened beyond that."

"Do you think Dakota would talk with me?" I asked.

"I think she will confirm the UFO, if you promise never to reveal her name. She believes nothing happened, and since she was unconscious most of the time, she doesn't remember much. "

After checking her soup and turning off the burner, Shawnee and I paid a visit to Dakota. She was very uneasy when I was introduced. As we sat down on her living room couch, she declared: "All I remember was the UFO, and I don't really want to talk about it. I've never been so scared in all of my life. UFOs are real. We saw it and then we were home. That is all I remember."

After thanking her for confirming Shawnee's sighting, we walked back the few blocks to Shawnee's house.

"There is one more question I have for you. How did you get home?" I asked.

"That's another strange thing," she said. "I have no memory of driving home. All I know is that I was suddenly in town and dropping Dakota off at her house. All I can think of is that the aliens brought us home."

I haven't seen Shawnee since our afternoon together, although she does keep in touch occasionally by email. There is no question that something happened to her that night on that lonely, isolated road. The biggest thing that has changed in her life is that she and Dakota never take their monthly trip to the city. Dakota never leaves the reservation.

Shawnee, on the other hand, goes to the city, but only when her husband is available to drive her.

8. EVERETT'S STORY:
THEY SAID MY BLOOD WAS DEFECTIVE

Everett worked in construction as a truck driver. His profession took him both on and off the reservation and often far from his home. In his early days, he admitted to being a hard drinker and a party man with women in many western states. One night on his way to the campsite of a new job, Everett had an encounter that changed his life forever. He agreed to tell me his story once I assured him anonymity.

I met Everett at an all-night truck stop in an off-reservation city near his home. He was waiting when I arrived. He stood as I approached the booth. He was about my height, five feet six. Overweight and suffering from asthma, he often wheezed when he spoke.

"It happened the summer after the big fire in Yellowstone National Park," he said after the waitress brought our ice tea.

"That would be in the late eighties. Correct?"

"The fire was in 1988. My encounter happened in 1989."

"Were you working in Yellowstone?" I asked.

"Yes. After the fire, many roads in Yellowstone needed major repairs. I applied to a crew that was working there. Because they were trying to fill a minority quota, I had no trouble getting the job. I hauled my travel trailer there and planned to live in the park that summer. That would cut down on costs, and the hourly wage was twice as much as I could earn locally. I knew it would be a good thing for my family. Work is scarcer in the winter. The salary could hold us over until another season. That's the way it is with construction workers. We either have tons of money or no money."

"Please tell me about your encounter."

"We were working in the Lake Lewis area. It was a place where the fire had melted the road in places. Do you know the area?"

I nodded.

"We worked at night most of the time. Huge halogen lights lit up the worksite so that we could work at night. During the day, thousands of tourists drove the one lane of the highway that was open. There were times we worked twenty-four-seven, but mostly the park officials wanted to keep a lane open for the tourists. I drove a truck and kept busy hauling gravel. I hauled gravel from one side of the lake to the other side where the repairs were going on."

"Was it near the lake you saw the UFO?"

"One night I was caught on the other side of the lake with dawn approaching. I watched as the lights were turned off, signaling the end of the work night. I parked the truck and headed for my vehicle. I planned to drive to my trailer and get some badly needed rest, when all of a sudden I saw this luminous object appear in the sky. It flew directly over the lake and hovered there. Suddenly this enormous spray of water erupted from the lake and touched the UFO. I think they were taking in water from the lake."

"How long did you see them take water from the lake?"

"Maybe five minutes. After that, I decided to get out of there before they saw me. I went into flight mode."

"Do you have any idea why you felt that way?"

"I felt like an electrical charge had hit my body. Then fear came over me. I just knew I had to flee."

"Did you get back to your travel trailer safely?"

"I wish," he said.

"What happened?"

"As I came around the lake, there was a field where I saw the craft land. I saw two luminous objects get out of the craft. I stopped my pickup to see what they were doing, and the next thing I knew they were outside my truck window peering in at me. Suddenly the engine stopped, the lights went out, and all I saw were two beings looking at me. I screamed at them to get away from me, but they didn't move. They stood there staring at me."

"Do you think they abducted you?" I asked.

"I know they took me onboard their craft. I struggled, but they came toward me and placed an instrument to my temple, and I became paralyzed. I couldn't even move a finger, and yet I was wide awake and able to know what was going on."

"What happened to you?"

"They removed my clothes and placed me in a small glass room. I was attached to a wall standing up. I don't know how they did it. I was paralyzed. Then these lights ran up and down my body. After a minute or so, they took me out. My body was covered with ash. They took me to another glass enclosure and put me in a chair. They attached these instruments to my arms and head and left me there. After a few minutes, they returned and took me to a room with a metal slab like you see in a vet's office. They placed me on the slab and began removing pieces of my hair. They took my blood, fingernails, and scrapped my skin."

"What were you doing while this was going on?"

"As I said, I was paralyzed. I could move my eyes, but I couldn't talk. I tried to move my toes, my fingers, my arms. Nothing. It was the worst feeling anyone could have. I didn't know if it was permanent or not. I kept thinking of my wife and kids and decided no job was worth this. I decided if I got out of this, I was going to attach my pickup to my trailer and head for home. I didn't care about the money. I just wanted to be home where I was safe."

"How did you escape the situation?"

"They told me my blood was defective."

"What do you mean?"

"After they tested my blood, they said it was defective and that they had no need of me. The next thing I knew, I was behind the wheel of my pickup and headed toward the campground."

"What did you do when you got back to your trailer?" I asked.

"I attached my pickup to the trailer and headed home. I stopped and told my boss I had a family emergency, and he gave me my paycheck and I headed for home. All the way home, I felt weak. I struggled to drive and keep the trailer on the road. I had to stop frequently and rest. I kept thinking it was the effects of the abduction."

"Did you go to the doctor?"

"Once I got back to the reservation, I went to the clinic. They sent me to the off-reservation hospital for further tests. I was diagnosed with leukemia."

"So do you think that they considered your blood defective because of the leukemia?"

"What else could it be? I shudder to think what they would have done to me had I been healthy. At least I know they will not be back." He smiled and took a long breath.

"How are you now?" I asked.

"I'm in remission. The leukemia was found in time. Fortunately, I had the type that was curable. I have to be monitored, but so far I'm doing fine."

"What can you tell me about the beings who abducted you?"

"Not much. They were luminous and covered from head to toe with a uniform like a hazmat suit. They wore goggles and a faceplate, so I really never saw their faces. I only remember they had a human shape, and although I never heard them talk out loud like you and I talk, I only knew they said my blood was defective. In a way, I'm lucky. Perhaps you could say they saved my life. On the other hand, I don't want to ever go through that ordeal again."

I have not seen Everett since our meeting, but I often think about him and the advanced technology of the aliens he encountered. They identified his problem and yet did nothing to help him. This was different from other individuals I had interviewed. In most cases, the victims were healed by their captors. I often wonder why Everett's case was different.

9. WARD'S STORY:
THE EARTH SWALLOWED THEM UP

Ward was an outgoing, easygoing man who loved slot machines and appreciated beautiful women. At least, this is how the self-identified Paiute Indian described himself. I met him in a casino in Las Vegas, Nevada. I had inadvertently taken over a slot machine that he had vacated and within seconds had hit the jackpot, which amounted to about $300 in nickels.

As the bells and whistles went off announcing a jackpot winner, he rushed to my side and said that the vacated slot machine was his. He had apparently left the machine to obtain more nickels. Feeling somewhat guilty that he had been feeding the slot machine for a couple of hours, I offered to share the winnings with him, which he refused, but then suggested that instead I could buy his dinner.

Ward was a tall, muscular man with a devilish smile who appeared never to have met a stranger. I was not surprised when he told me he was a lawyer. His persuasive manner of speaking revealed a man who was educated and articulate. As we walked to one of the casino's buffets, every woman we passed smiled and acknowledged him. On each occasion, he returned their greetings and tipped his black cowboy hat, which seemed to be a permanent extension of his body. As the evening wore on, I explained to him that I was on my way to Arizona to meet up with some contacts for my next book. He became extremely interested when I told him I collected stories of encounters with UFOs.

"I saw my first UFO when I was about twelve," he said. "Perhaps you would like to tell my story."

"I'd love to hear your story," I replied as he got up to make a second trip to the buffet. When he returned, I waited until he finished talking with a young woman who stopped at our table and invited him to a party.

"I was with my grandfather in the Mojave Desert," he began. "We went there on a camp out. The Panamint Mountains were sacred to him. So each year, from about the age of eight to eighteen, I made that annual trip with him. We camped, we walked trails, and we prayed. At night he would tell me the ancient stories of the Paiute."

He paused when a man approached our table and greeted him. They spoke long enough for Ward to inform his friend Hudson that I was a famous writer who had invited him to dinner. While they both laughed and talked, I remained silent and enjoyed their bantering. When Everett left, he apologized: "Sorry, but I have to live up to my reputation."

"I'm more interested in your story than an apology," I said, trying to ignore the fact that he had led Hudson to believe that I was a woman so in need of male companionship that I would pay for his dinner.

"When Grandpa took me camping, we didn't stay in organized campgrounds. Grandpa had a secret place, a place where we could camp away from prying eyes. It gave us a better view of the night skies, and we couldn't hear other people, just the sounds of nature. Our evening ritual was to cook dinner and afterwards add a couple of huge logs to the fire until it blazed into the sky. My grandpa always brought marshmallows. He said he brought them for me, but I knew he loved them just as much. After the fire was blazing hot and our dinner had settled, he sent me to get the bag of marshmallows from the pickup. Suddenly I heard him call out for me to hurry up. I heard the urgency in his voice, grabbed the bag, and headed back to camp. I wasn't prepared for what I saw. There, hovering near our campsite, was a UFO. It was no more than two-hundred feet above the ground, so we were able to see the complete outline as it blocked out the stars above."

"Can you describe the UFO?"

"It was about the length of a football field. It was oblong, like a tube. It made no noise and appeared suspended in mid-air. It was not moving at all. It was dark, not shiny. I couldn't make out a color. There were several white, dim lights underneath it, and one in the front that was like a strobe light. In fact, the light came very near our campsite as it searched the surroundings. I remember being very afraid."

"How did your grandfather react?"

"He told me to stay calm. He said they wouldn't hurt us."

"How long did it stay in that position?"

"We watched it for several minutes, and then it began to move toward the Panamints and away from us. I will never forget it. It moved slowly as though preparing for a special maneuver. As it neared the mountain, the strobe light became more intense and the craft moved slower and slower, when suddenly it was as though the mountains opened up and the craft moved inside."

"Do you mean that the UFO went inside the Paramints?"

"That's exactly what happened."

"Did you see it come out of the mountains?"

"We decided to sit up all night and keep a vigil. Grandpa put on another pot of coffee. We roasted marshmallows. Along toward midnight, we saw the huge craft come out of the mountains and land on the desert floor. I watched my grandfather take the coffee pot and douse our fire. As we sat in our secret spot, we watched as several tall beings came out of the craft and walked to a spot no more than fifty feet from us. As we watched, we saw the earth open up and the beings disappeared under the desert floor."

"What do you mean, they disappeared under the desert floor?" I asked.

"That's exactly what happened. It was like the earth swallowed them up."

"Did you see anything else?" I asked.

"There were six of them that went under the earth, but about an hour later, eight came out of the earth and boarded the craft and were gone in an instant."

"You saw six go down inside the earth, but eight came out. Correct?"

"Yes."

"What did you think had happened?"

"We knew it confirmed the ancient legends. You see, our grandfathers of long ago told stories about a white race of people who wore pure white clothes and lived inside the mountain. He said that some believe their original home was underground. They built a complete civilization there, away from the eyes of humans."

"Do you believe those stories?"

"I believe what we witnessed confirmed there is a civilization under the Mojave Desert and in the Panamint Mountains inhabited by Star People. But what's more important is that my grandfather believed."

"And you?"

"I saw the UFO disappear inside the mountain. I know I was only twelve years old, but I saw what I saw. I saw it with my grandfather, and although we agreed not to tell anyone that doesn't mean it didn't happen. It was real."

"Why did you agree not to tell anyone?"

"My grandfather felt it was a sacred event only meant for the two of us."

"Did you ever see the UFO again?"

"Many times. We went back to the site every year until I was eighteen. That was the year my grandfather died. We made one last trip. At that time, he told me this would be our last trip and our last time to see the Star People, and almost on cue, they appeared. It was an answer to my prayers. I wanted so badly for them to return one last time. My grandfather had cancer, and we knew that he didn't have long to live, but even then, he wanted to go there. We sat up at night and toasted marshmallows. Along about midnight, they came. They performed the same ritual. The UFO went inside the mountain, and in an hour or so it came out of the mountain and landed on the desert floor. This time eight men went down inside the desert floor, but this time only six came out. But

I will never forget that night. Seems like ancient history now, but I'm glad to have the opportunity to share it with you. I hope you will include it in your book."

"I want you to think back to the incidents. You said that when you were twelve, you saw six beings go under the desert floor and eight come out. On your last trip, you saw eight go below but only six came out. I am interested in knowing if those who came out were dressed the same as those who went below. Do you remember?"

"That's a very interesting question. My grandfather remarked about that both times. The ones that who went into the space craft were dressed in shiny, silver suits. The ones who came from below were dressed in white, not in form fitting suits, but in rather loose garments."

"How did your grandfather account for that?"

"He believed that the ones who came out were going home to their birth planet, and the ones staying were their replacements. That made him even more convinced that there was a secret civilization under the Mojave Desert."

"Did your grandfather or you ever communicate with them?" I asked.

"On our final trip, my grandfather stood and walked toward them. I stood in the shadows and watched. My grandfather warned me to stay away. When he reached the craft, at first they paid no attention to him, and then they turned in his direction and greeted him."

"Did he communicate with them?" I asked.

"Grandpa said they told him they would see him in the stars."

"Did he explain what they meant by that?"

"My grandfather believed that death was not the end of life. He believed that when he left Earth, he would move onto another place, another planet, another world. He felt they were telling him they knew his destiny and that they would meet again. Perhaps he would even be reborn as a star man and revisit the desert."

"Have you ever returned to that sacred spot now that you are an adult?"

"Never. Every year I think about it, but I'm afraid it would not be the same without my grandpa."

"Have you ever considered that if you go there, you might meet your grandfather as a star man?"

"Believe me, I have thought about that, but I guess I'm not able to handle it if that did occur. I prefer to think that he's alive and well among the stars, and that he watches after me."

"Do you think he would be proud of the man you've become?"

"I don't think so. Grandpa did not like gambling of any form. That's probably the real reason I don't go there. If I should meet him, I'm sure he would let me know his displeasure with me."

"Have you ever considered changing your life?"

"Seeing that UFO changed me. I come here to forget."

"Why do you need to forget?"

"I know there are millions of people who would like to see what I have seen. But for some reason, I want to stay on Earth, live my life, and when I pass I want it to be final. I don't have any desire to live among the stars."

"Is there anything else that you can think of about the encounter that you might have left out?"

Ward thought for a moment. "Nothing. I told you exactly what I saw."

I spent the evening with Ward at the slot machines. While I am not one to stay at a slot machine more than five or ten minutes, Ward had a habit of selecting one machine and staying there. Over the course of the night, we became friends, and I always see him when I go to Las Vegas. The last time I saw him, he offered to take me to the Mojave Desert to see the Panamint Mountains and camp out at the spot where he saw the UFO. I was surprised at his change of heart. He said it had something to do with middle age and his recent open heart surgery. Whatever the case, I plan on taking him up on his offer.

10. LEONARD'S STORY: THEY LIFTED US TO SAFE WATERS

Leonard was a professional fisherman by trade. His career began at sixteen, and at seventy-two he piloted a boat with his two nephews. While fishing was his livelihood, it also provided sustenance for his family and his dogs. An Athabasca Native, he practiced the traditional ceremonies and teachings of his people. I met him at a potlatch when he approached me and asked if I was still in the business of collecting UFO stories. When I told him that I would probably collect them on my deathbed, he looked at me and said that he had a story to tell and that he wanted to tell it before he was on his deathbed.

I met Leonard in the restaurant at the Sophie Station Hotel where I was staying in Fairbanks the next evening. Since Fairbanks served as his winter home, it was convenient for both of us. Outside, the snow was blowing sideways underneath the streetlights. I found a place near the window for a good view of the street and kept warm with hot tea while waiting his arrival. When he walked in the door, he spotted me immediately and waved. Leonard was one of the happiest men I had ever met. He was always smiling and had a greeting for everyone whether friend or stranger. A tall, barrel-chested man with a small goatee, he reached across the table and shook my hand before removing his fur-lined parka.

"I hope you haven't been waiting long," he said, as he sat down across of me.

I shook my head. "I've been watching the storm."

"I heard the weather forecast. We might get a foot tonight. Strange weather we are having here in Alaska. Last year, it was warm; this year, one storm after another."

After the waitress took our order, we talked about the potlatch and the importance of the traditional gathering. When our meal was served, Leonard spoke in a soft, deliberate voice about his encounter.

"I've spent my life on a fishing boat. I started out as a boy on my uncle's boat and learned the ropes. Saved every dime I made and eventually put a down payment on my own boat. I've been deep sea fishing most of my life, except for a stint in the army."

"Were you in Vietnam?" I asked.

"Yes."

"Did you see UFOs in Vietnam?"

"Several times, but they never came close. I saw them three times in battle, just hovering in the sky as though they were observing. I never saw them land, but I always wondered about them: What kind of beings would be on the spaceships?"

"When did you have the encounter you want to tell me about?" I asked.

"It was three years ago. The boys and I were fishing for tuna. We were late returning to shore. We'd had a good day. We'd filled all of our ice chests. It was hard to give up on a day like that, so when we headed for the harbor it was getting dusk."

"So you are talking early morning, since it really never gets dark in Alaska in the summer. "

"Correct. But most of the boats had returned to harbor. In fact, I saw no others. It was peaceful. The waters were calm, when suddenly the boat was caught up in a whirlpool that came out of nowhere."

"A whirlpool? Can you explain?"

"A fierce wind came up and all of a sudden it was like we were caught in a water tornado, a whirlpool that sucked our boat downward into the water. I looked up, and there was a wall of water all around us. It was a clockwise spinning funnel swirling downward, and we were being sucked into it. I thought we were doomed when something unexpected occurred. Overhead I saw lights, bright lights in a circle pattern, and a force that I cannot explain reached out and picked us up, flew us through the air, and placed us in calm waters."

"What do you mean, a force flew you through the air?"

"That's exactly what happened. One time we were swirling down and down into this funnel of water with no means of escape, and the next thing I know we were lifted out of the tunnel and flying through the sky. We were taken away from the whirlpool and carefully placed on calm seas. It was unbelievable."

"What were your nephews doing?"

"My nephews were on deck and hanging onto the railing for dear life and screaming my name at the top of their lungs. I climbed down to the deck and looked in the direction they were pointing. There was a spacecraft hovering over the sea about fifty yards from us."

"What were they doing?"

"I could see the water was turbulent below the craft much like the whirlpool we had encountered. In the middle of the whirlpool was a stream of water, maybe twenty inches or so being sucked up into the spacecraft. It was at the same time a beautiful and frightening sight. At that moment, I realized that we had been caught up in a whirlpool made by this craft, and they had saved us by lifting us out of the water and placing us in calm waters."

"As you watched the event, did you think of calling the Coast Guard?"

"I not only attempted to call the Coast Guard, but I put a call out to any fishing vessels in the area, but my radio was not working. There was not even any static. When I tried to start the engine, it was dead. We were dead in the water. We could not flee or notify anyone if we wanted to."

"What did you do?"

"By this time, my nephews had joined me in the cabin. We stood there and watched the scene unfold before us. There was nothing else we could do."

"How long did you watch the spacecraft?"

"Maybe ten or fifteen minutes."

"At any time did you see any beings?"

"No, but I know that it was flown by intelligent beings. That is the only way I can explain the way they lifted us out of the water. They saved our lives, but the problem was created by them in the first place."

"You said you watched the craft for ten or fifteen minutes taking on water. What happened after that?" I asked.

"It rose into the sky and then suddenly turned on its side and skidded along the water like a water skier and then climbed and climbed until it was out of sight. I had never seen any craft operate in such a fashion. It was amazing."

"Did you ever report your sighting?" I asked.

"I did report it to the Coast Guard. They looked at me like I was hallucinating, filled out a report and I never heard another word."

"Did you tell other fisherman?"

"No. After the reception I received from the Coast Guard, I decided to keep my mouth shut. I told the boys to do the same. I told my mother, Ruth, about what happened, and she knew about you. She said her brother had talked to you at his fish camp on the Tanana. So that's the reason I contacted you. I wanted to know if you had heard similar stories."

"I have heard similar stories. I've had individuals tell me stories about watching spaceships siphon water out of rivers and lakes. So I'm not surprised to hear your story. You've had a unique experience, but you are definitely not alone in your encounter."

"Thank you so much. I needed confirmation." He smiled and patted his stomach. "I'm ready for some dessert," he said.

I agreed.

I have not seen Leonard since our meeting, but out of sight does not mean I do not think of him. I am planning to attend a gathering of singers and dancers at the university. It is an annual affair in Fairbanks, and I am hoping I will see him there. His story of the alien spacecraft lifting his fishing boat out of a deadly situation they created made an impression on me. It is not the first time, however that I've heard of star people rescuing those in distress.

11. EVE'S STORY: THE STAR PEOPLE ARE HEALERS

Eve graduated with a Masters in Biology from a state university. Unable to find work related to her discipline, Eve took a job in the Social Services Department of the tribe, authorizing food stamps for needy families. Margie, Eve's mother, was a retired tribal council member who was housebound from a debilitating form of arthritis. I had watched Eve grow up, as her mother and I had been friends for years, so I was not surprised when I got a phone call at my motel one night inviting me to dinner the following evening. The big surprise came when I discovered the invitation was not just a chance to eat Margie's famous Indian tacos, but an opportunity to hear one of the most interesting stories about a UFO encounter I had ever heard.

I arrived at Margie's house two hours before dinner. Although it was a Saturday, I was surprised to see Eve at home as well. "I told Evan [Eve's husband] it was strictly a girls' night so he drove over to see Eric LeBeau," she explained. After two hours of small talk about relatives, reservation politics, Margie's retirement, the family garden, and Eve's plan to expand the house, we went into the kitchen where Margie and Eve began preparing dinner.

After eating the best Indian tacos in a year, we retired to the porch again with our coffee. "I had Mom invite you for dinner tonight. I remember how you loved her Indian tacos, but there was another reason. Something happened to us a few months back that changed our lives, especially Mom's. We wanted to talk to you about it because we trust you and we know what we say tonight will be used discretely."

"What is this about?"

"A UFO," Eve responded. She paused and looked at Margie. "Have you noticed any change in Mom since the last time you saw her?"

"It looks like retirement has been good for her," I said, "She seems to get around better."

Margie nodded.

"It's the Star People," said Eve. "But we have to go back to the beginning. Mom, you were the first to see them."

"It all started with a raccoon," Margie began. "There was this pesky raccoon that kept coming around at night. He uprooted my garden plants, he destroyed my green beans, and he picked the green tomatoes and threw them on the ground. He was very destructive. So one night, I decided to put an end to him for good. I got my .22 rifle and went out to the windbreak." I knew she was referring to the band of trees planted on the north and west side of the house to protect it from the winds. "I had one of those new flashlights with a spotlight. I planned to find him and shoot him."

"Mom's a good shot," Eve said. "You know that. I remember the two of you target practicing in the backyard. The two of you were so competitive." She laughed.

I ignored her comment, although I knew she had been perceptive about our competitive nature. "Did you find the raccoon?" I asked, trying to keep the conversation on track.

"I found more than that," Margie said. "I found a man, a star man."

"Do you mean a man was destroying your garden?"

"No, that was the raccoon."

"I don't understand."

"When I went out to the windbreak, I was shining my spotlight about, and suddenly I saw a human form walking toward me. I shined the spotlight in his direction, and he kind of yelped and covered his eyes with his arms. I lowered the light and asked him to identify himself while keeping him in my sights."

"Were you pointing the gun at him?"

"You bet. I didn't recognize him—who goes around somebody's

house and hides out in the windbreak? I'd shoot him in a minute if he came toward me. I wouldn't aim to kill, just to stop him. I'm not a killer, but I will defend myself."

"You said you saw a human form. I'm curious why you chose those words to describe what you saw."

"Because I was looking for an animal but saw a human, but then I discovered he wasn't a human at all."

"What did you do next?"

"When I demanded to know who he was, he stopped and said, 'Don't be afraid. I mean no harm.' I lowered my gun and shined the light on him again. He looked human—at least he had a human form. He wore a dark brown one-piece uniform. A white label on his arm was stamped with unfamiliar characters. He later told me that it identified his role on his planet."

"What was his role?

"He was a doctor and researcher, as best I understood. He was part of a team of individuals traveling the universe collecting items for study."

"Where were the others?" I asked.

"They were deposited in different sites around the Earth."

"Deposited?"

"That's what he said. Deposited."

"What else did he tell you?"

"That he planned to stay in the area for three more days and that it was important that no one else would learn of his existence."

"It was about that time that I joined Mama in the windbreak," Eve said. "I was shocked when I saw the man standing there. I thought we were in danger and grabbed Mama's rifle and aimed it at him. Mama grabbed the .22 back and told me he wasn't dangerous. I didn't know how that could be. He looked dangerous to me."

"What do you mean?" I asked.

"I'd never seen anyone dressed liked that," Eve said. "No one around here dressed like him and that told me he wasn't from the reservation. He had very strange eyes. They were huge and black, and you couldn't see a pupil. He was sensitive to light and shielded his eyes every time light came near him."

"How could you tell he had no pupils?"

"You know how pupils glow in the dark when light hits them? His eyes didn't glow. In fact, every time a light came near him, he backed away, almost in terror."

"What did you decide to do?" I asked.

"I told him he could stay," Margie said, "but that he would have to stay in the barn."

"I objected to that," said Eve. "I was afraid he would scare my horse. She is skittish anyway, and I didn't want her frightened."

"Finally," said Margie, "we decided he could stay in the green house. There was a tool shed attached to the greenhouse. I figured he could stay there in the dark if he needed to. He seemed to like the idea of the greenhouse. He was interested in plants, and it was warm and humid there. He said that on his planet it was cold on the surface, but his people lived underground where it was warmer and more moist than Earth. The greenhouse made him feel at home. We led him to the greenhouse, but I think he already knew about it. He asked us about various plants. He was interested in my herbs and wanted to know their uses."

"Could you describe him?" I asked.

"He was about five feet eight," Eve commented. "He was taller than us by a little bit. We are both five feet six. Very slim. A prairie wind would blow him away. He walked funny, like he skimmed the ground. He didn't take steps the way we did, but I think it was because of the funny backpack he had."

"What do you mean about a funny backpack?" I asked.

"It was a square pack," Eve explained. "I saw him push a button on his sleeve when he moved. I positioned myself behind him as he followed Mama to the greenhouse. I wanted to get a better look at him. I shined the light on him, and he rushed forward. That's when I noticed his feet never really touched the ground."

"Once you took him to the greenhouse, what kind of interchange did you have with him?"

"I have a wicker chair in the greenhouse," Margie replied. "It has cushions. I told him he could rest there because he appeared weak. I asked him if he needed water or food and he said no. He had everything he needed."

"Did you ever get a look at his face?" I asked.

"Only glimpses that night," Eve said. " But later we saw his face. It was a little human, from what I could tell, except for the big eyes. His mouth was small. A stretchy cap covered his head. I don't know if he had hair. His skin was rather pasty. He would never pass for human in a crowd, unless he was out at Halloween."

"And yet, you agreed for him to stay on your place. How do you explain that?"

"I felt at peace around him," Margie said. "He told me he wouldn't harm me and I believed him. I saw no weapon. I trusted him."

"I didn't want to trust him," said Eve, "but I felt an overwhelming sense of peace too, and along with that feeling, a need to protect him. When I think about it now, I think he controlled our minds, but I think he was harmless. Perhaps he did it so we would not shoot him."

"Did you communicate with him after the night you met him?"

"I did," said Eve. "I went to the greenhouse the next morning and found him examining the plants. He had large black goggles over his eyes. He explained that his eyes were not used to the light. He said the light on his planet was more like the twilight of earth. I asked him about old age and diseases on his planet. I had been worried about Mama for a long time. Not only did she suffer from fibromyalgia, but also her arthritis had become crippling. There were days she couldn't get out of bed without my help. I wanted to know if they had such diseases on his planet."

"What did he tell you?"

"He said that diseases were not a part of their being."

"I didn't understand that, and he did not understand the disease I was describing. When I told him that fibromyalgia as I understood it had something to do with short-circuiting in the nervous system, he became very interested. The next time I talked with him, he said he could cure Mama."

"And did he?"

"Why do you think you see such a change in me?" Margie said. "His hands had magic in them. He asked me to lie flat on my bed."

"Did you let him in the house?"

"Oh, yes," said Eve. "There was no place to lie flat in the greenhouse. I convinced Mama to let him try."

"The moment he touched me, I felt this warmth engulf my body. It became uncomfortable at one point, but nothing unbearable."

"Were you afraid?"

"No, I knew he wouldn't harm me."

"How did you know?" I asked.

"I just knew. It took no longer than a minute, and he told me that I would have no more pain."

"Have you?"

"No," Margie said. "For the past six months, I have felt like a new woman. I can do the things of my youth."

"She is stronger than me," Eve added. "I can't believe how he cured her. Look at her hands. She was so bad she couldn't open a doorknob or a jar. Now she does those things with ease. Her hands are no longer disfigured. Not only is her arthritis gone, her fibromyalgia is non-existent, and her diabetes and heart disease are gone. When she went to the specialist, he told her he wanted some of what she had been taking. Mama couldn't tell him the truth. No one would believe her, but she is living proof that the star people are healers. They don't need medicine. Only their hands. It's like the power our elders used to have. All they did was lay hands on the sick to cure them. Most have lost that power, but the star men still have it."

"I told him when he left," Margie said, "that he was welcome to come back anytime. If he does, I want you to come and let him heal you. You will feel like a young woman again. It will give you the energy and the stamina to live life again."

I did not hear from Margie or Eve for over a year. One night, I got a call from Eve. She told me her mother was still youthful and disease free, but the Star Man had not returned. I cannot help but envy Margie. Who wouldn't want the chance to be youthful and disease-free again?

12. ROY'S STORY: THEY GO INSIDE THE MOUNTAIN

Roy lived alone in the cabin where he was born. The property had been in his family since the government allotment of assigned plots of land to individuals. A veteran who was known for his sharp shooting skills, Roy provided for himself by hunting, raising chickens and a milk cow, and growing a garden. On occasion, the women from the church would give him fresh fruit and jellies when he made it to the small Catholic church located closest to his remote property. On Christmas they made him enough cookies, fruitcake, and candy to last him throughout the year. It took him the better part of a day to preserve the gifts. He said he used the magic of the Star People. The priest at the church told me about Roy. When he suggested I talk with Roy, he said he was not sure if Roy was mentally incapacitated or if he actually was visited by aliens, but he felt Roy would welcome my visit.

On my next trip to the reservation, I stopped at Huckleberry's Health Food Store and loaded up on dried fruits and vegetables and added unhealthy snacks like Snowballs, brownies, and Honeybuns. I finished off my collection with cans of freeze dried hamburger, chicken, and beef chunks from the Honeyville survival section. On my way home, I stopped at the Smoke Shoppe and bought several tins of loose tobacco. I left early on Saturday morning so that I would make it to my destination by late that night. I planned on attending the church services on Sunday and get directions from the priest to Roy's cabin.

When I arrived at Roy's cabin, he was finishing his breakfast dishes. I introduced myself to him, and he welcomed me into his cabin. He pulled out a chair and indicated I should sit, while he filled a cup of coffee and placed it in front of me. He put the last of his dishes in a drainer, picked up his coffee cup, and sat down across of me.

"I don't get much visitors out here. I'm surprised you made it."

"My Subaru is four-wheel drive and can go places few dare to go," I said, smiling.

I looked at the man who sat across from me. He was very thin and looked like he needed a good meal. Neighbors told me he was the shell of the man who went to Vietnam, and I understood their description. Following a disastrous marriage and diagnosed with PTSD, he had chosen to live alone in an isolated cabin to avoid interaction with people instead of taking the prescription drugs provided by the VA. He had a nervous tick above his left eye, which caused him to occasionally bury his eyes in his hands and rub his eyes and forehead vigorously.

"Speaking of the Subaru," I continued, "I have a couple of boxes of goodies in my Outback for you."

"Gifts are always welcome," he said. He got up and headed out the door. I followed him outside and opened the hatch. He quickly examined the contents and smiled. "It's Christmas," he declared as he carried one box inside and returned quickly for the second. "Thank you so much. Without friends, my diet would be very limited." I watched as he examined the boxes, picked up a package of Snowballs, held them high, and said they were his favorite. He sat down at the table and opened the package. He took out one of the chocolate/marshmallow cupcake balls and began eating, but not before offering one to me. As he ate, I approached the subject of the Star People.

"Father Finnegan told me that you have told him stories about the Star People and your interaction with them. I write books about American Indian encounters with the Star People. I wondered if you would talk with me about your experiences. I promise to keep everything anonymous. No one will ever know your name or location. What do you think?"

He looked at me with a blank look on his face, finished off his

Snowball, retrieved the coffee pot, and refilled his cup. When he offered to replenish mine, I shook my head.

"I believe if you give me something," he said, "I give something back. That's the Indian way. So to repay you, I will tell you about the Star People. I don't fault Father Finnegan for telling you about them, but I don't tell a lot of people. They think I'm crazy when I'm only telling the truth."

"Please don't feel obligated to me. I didn't bring food so you would feel obliged to tell me your story. I brought it out of respect for you. If you don't feel comfortable, I will leave."

"No." He reached out and touched my hand. "I don't want you to go. Perhaps it's time everyone knows the truth."

"Please, start at the beginning."

"The first time I saw them I was so frightened I couldn't move. I was probably about ten years old. I was unaware of their presence until they were practically on top of me. It was the lights, the brightest lights I ever saw that caught my attention. When I looked up, I saw this huge round machine above me. I saw two small balls of light come out of it and fly off. Then I saw the big craft move upward and disappear from sight. Only then did I come out of my hiding place and hurry home."

"Where were you when this happened?"

"About two miles from here. I always rode my horse, Bella, to school. In those days, all the kids came by horse, walked, or were delivered in wagons. The school had a fenced in meadow for the horses. Bella liked it there. She got to socialize with the other horses, and there was always hay brought in by the parents. On this particular day, I got in trouble with the teacher. She made me stay after school, and it was late in the evening. It gets dark early in the winter. I was thinking about how I was going to explain to Mom and Pap about my delayed homecoming when I saw it. I felt Bella tense under me. I held onto her reigns and guided her into the wooded area." He paused and took a sip of his coffee.

"Is that where you hid?"

He nodded.

"You'll see it on your way back to town. It's on the left side of the road. A stand of willows and Aspen. Anyway, Bella and I hid there and watched. After the big craft was gone, we raced home."

"So what did you think you had seen at ten years of age?" I asked.

"The boys at school were always trading comic books. There were many stories about space men and space travel. Buck Rogers was my hero. I still have a couple of the old comics. He pointed to a three-foot-tall stack of magazines in the corner of the room. I'll look for them after we finish our interview."

"Are you telling me that you thought you saw a spaceship?"

"Yes. The next day I told Hinson and Joseph. They were my best friends. They believed me, and every Saturday they would spend the night at my house, and we'd watch for them. In the summer, we'd camp out and watch for them."

"Did you ever see them?"

"Not until we were about twelve. I remember we were in the sixth grade that year. We asked the teacher if she thought there was life in outer space, and she told us that God only created humans because they were in his image. She said any thought of beings in outer space was the Devil infiltrating our brains. Needless to say, we never asked her anything about space travel after that."

"You said you saw them when you were twelve. Can you tell me about that?"

"Sure. It was nighttime. The three of us had gone night fishing down on the river. We had a tent and some soup beans my mother made. Joseph brought some cornbread, and we had slices of chocolate cake from Hinson's mom. We thought we were set for the night. Along toward midnight, we were waiting for strikes, when the spacecraft came. This time, a ball of light came out and we watched it descend to the ground, very close to where we were fishing. Joseph grabbed his flashlight, and we went in the direction of the landing. As we neared a clearing, we saw a round craft setting in an opening near the river. We dropped to our bellies and watched. We saw two figures milling around the craft. Hinson was very frightened and stood up to run. His actions caught the attention of the two figures, and almost immediately they surrounded us. I looked at Hinson, thinking he escaped, but instead it was like he was paralyzed in a running position. I remember hearing my heartbeat and that's all."

"What did the figures do with you?"

"The next thing we knew, we were inside the craft. It was not very big. It was only one big room. There were five beings inside. They told us not to be afraid and that they were friends. Hinson was crying hysterically. I watched as one of the beings walked over to him. He had something in his hand that looked like a futuristic gun, and he pressed it to his shoulder and almost immediately Hinson stopped crying, laid down, and fell asleep. Joseph got up and tried to find an exit, fighting with all of his might, when one of the beings brought him back to a table. Once on the table, he couldn't move."

"Can you describe the beings?"

"I kept thinking about the Tiger Men that Buck Rogers found on Mars. They walked like humans, they had human form, but their eyes were catlike."

"Do you remember anything that happened on board the ship?" I asked.

"I watched them examine Hinson and Joseph. I saw them take clippings of hair and scrapings of skin. They had a machine they used over the eyes and head. When it was my turn, they did the same thing. But even though my friends were asleep, I was fully awake. I didn't try to resist them. I knew if I cooperated, I might learn something."

"Did you?"

"Only that they came from the stars and they were explorers. I asked them about life on other planets, and they told me many worlds exist. That's about it. They asked me our ages, and I told them we were all twelve. After that, they took us back to our campsite. Hinson and Joseph were still unconscious, but they told me it was only temporary. After that, they were gone."

"Did you ever feel threatened by them?"

"Never. In fact, just the opposite. I felt happy around them. Even though they were strange looking, I felt we had just confirmed the Buck Rogers' comics. Life did exist on other worlds and I was excited about it."

"When your friends regained consciousness, did they remember anything?"

"Hinson remembered seeing the beings coming toward us. Joseph remembered being on the ship but not what happened to him. I was the only one with full memory. That night we made a pact never to reveal our experience."

"When did you see them the next time?"

"In Vietnam. Joseph and I had enlisted together and stayed together. We were both in the same squad in Vietnam. Hinson failed the military physical. Ever since we had been abducted, he developed a rash on his body. When the military doctors saw it, they failed him. They didn't know what it was."

"Where did you see them in Vietnam?"

"Joseph and I were on point. We were about a half mile ahead of the others when we encountered the same cat-like man. He told us to follow him and we did. He asked us why we were fighting. Joseph told him we were fighting the VC. He asked again, and I told him we did not understand why we were fighting. He asked us if we wanted to go home. We told him yes, and the next thing we knew we were back on the reservation."

"Are you telling me they took you from the battlefield back to the reservation?"

"That's exactly what happened."

"We knew we were in trouble. We would either be listed as MIA or as deserters. We asked them to return us. They were confused by our demands but complied. We could not tell our commanding officer what had happened to us, so we told him we got lost. He didn't buy our story and threw us in the brig. We stayed there until our enlistment was up. We were given dishonorable discharges and sent home."

"So you never told your commanding officer what happened, correct?"

"Nope. He wouldn't have believed us anyway."

"When we got home, my father was not happy about my discharge. He felt I had dishonored the family. So I lived in the barn for the longest time. In the summers, I camped out by the river. Every day I would return home and help him on the ranch. It was about two years before he asked me to move home."

"What about Joseph?"

"Joseph took to drinking. He got killed about twenty years ago by a hit and run driver. His homicide was never solved."

"And Hinson?"

"Hinson died while we were in Vietnam. The doctors' said his body had been poisoned."

"So it leaves only you. Have you seen the Star Men again?"

"Many, many times." He paused, chose another cupcake, and ate it before continuing. "I want to show you something," he said, standing.

I got up from the table and followed him out the door. He opened the door of his battered pickup truck and waited for me to climb inside. He got in the pickup and pointed it toward the single lane gravel road that led to town. We traveled only a couple of miles before he pulled off the side of the road.

"Are these the trees where you first saw the Star Men?" I asked.

"Same ones, but we need to get out and walk from here."

I slid out of the pickup onto the gravel road. I followed him as he meandered in and among the trees until we came to the river bank. "It's just another half mile."

"Where are we going?" I asked.

"This is where we camped," he said, as he paused and caught his breath.

Then, he continued following the river.

"I believe they come here because they have a secret," he said.

"What kind of secret?"

"Do you see that mountain up there?"

"Yes."

"I've seen them go inside that mountain. They've taken me inside the mountain while I was on their spaceship."

"What do they do inside the mountain?"

"I don't know. All I know is that they have taken me on board their craft and then the next thing I know, we land."

"What do they do when they take you on board?"

"They do the same thing every time. They are interested in aging of the human species. But after I came back from the war, they did other things."

"Can you tell me?"

"It is not something I should talk about to a lady."

"Does it have to do with procreation?"

"I don't know the word. But I can tell you it has to do with taking something from me that they can use to make babies."

I nodded. "I understand."

"I've spent years trying to locate where they go. A few weeks ago, I was fishing. I was sitting about where you are standing. I saw a craft come out of the mountain. At first, I didn't believe my eyes, but now I know it's the truth. They have a base inside the mountain. Two nights ago, I was night fishing and I saw a craft disappear inside the mountain. It never came out, and I stayed up all night and watched. I don't know what they do there, but I believe that's their home away from their planet. I'm too old to go there and check it out. It is too high up, and I'd have to be a rock climber to even consider it, but I'm telling you, they go inside that mountain. That's why I always see them in this area."

"Has anyone else seen them?"

"As far as I know, only my old, departed buddies and me."

"But you told the priest about it, didn't you?"

"Oh, no. I talked to the priest about life in the universe one day. He hired me to do some work around the church, and we got into a conversation. I told him I had seen a UFO and that they come here often. He probably thinks I'm crazy, but I assure you, I'm not. I know they exist, just as Joseph and Hinson knew. I think they're the reason my friends are dead. Joseph because he turned to alcohol to deal with his dishonorable discharge, and Hinson because he was exposed to something on their spaceship."

"What do you think it might have been?"

"Hinson was the only one of the three of us that was rendered unconscious. I think whatever that being used to quiet him caused the rash and literally destroyed his body."

"Do you believe they are evil?"

"I don't think they believe themselves to be evil, but I don't think they consider the consequences of what they do. In a way, they appear naive. When we were in 'Nam, and they asked us if we wished we were home, we said, yes, but that did not mean we wanted to leave. Every marine wants to be home, but they took us home. That tells me they do not completely understand the human race. Perhaps that's the reason for their tests; they are trying to learn."

"How would you describe the impact your encounters have had on your life?" I asked.

"It has controlled my life. From the time I was a boy, I was obsessed with these space travelers. When I came home, I wanted to reconnect with them. I have always gone willingly and participated in their experiments. I want to believe they are good, but I'm not sure. Even now, I come here to see them. It has become an obsession."

In the late afternoon, we returned to the cabin. Roy loaded up a small pack with canned beans and hard tack. He invited me to join him for another vigil at the river. We sat up all night and watched the mountain. We ate the beans and the tasteless bread for dinner and two carrot cake cupcakes I had brought for a treat. He made three pots of cowboy coffee to keep us awake. Along toward 3 a.m., we saw a ball of light in the sky. We watched as it came close to where we were camping and then take a sharp right turn and disappear inside the mountain. Afterward, we gathered our things and made our way to the pickup and back to the safety of his cabin.

"You saw it, didn't you?" he asked.
"I saw it," I said.

I have visited with Roy twice since our interview. Each time I spend the weekend, I come prepared to join him at his secluded campsite by the river. I always bring boxes of chocolate marshmallow snowballs which have become a staple in our campout diet. As I join him in his all-night vigil, I can't help but think the Star People know he is there, but they do not care. After all, he has carried their secret with him for nearly sixty years. There is no need to think he will ever reveal their secret to another person. I am blessed that he chose me.

13. JOSEPH'S STORY: NOT ALL OF THEIR ABDUCTEES ARE HUMAN

Sometimes I come across stories of encounters in the most unusual places and under the most extraordinary situations. One day in January, I was headed for a small airport located about forty miles from a reservation town where I had agreed to help a local school district develop a Safe Schools grant. I hate flying in small airplanes, particularly during bad weather. After a three-hour delay, the plane was cleared for takeoff. I found myself seated next to a man who was dressed in a uniform identical to our pilot's. As the plane left the runway, he introduced himself to me as Joseph and told me that he was headed home to the reservation to see his grandfather, who was in the hospital. A half-hour into the flight, the pilot came on the intercom and explained that we had encountered a severe blizzard and were being rerouted to another airport more than a hundred miles from our destination. As I exited the plane, I saw Joseph engaged in a lively conversation with the baggage handler. As we were hustled into the small airport lounge to await transportation to a nearby motel for the night, I distinctly heard the baggage handler mention "a UFO" that had been sighted. As we lined up to board a bus provided by the airline, I held back and waited for Joseph, hoping for a chance to find out about the UFO. When he joined the line, I turned toward him and discreetly asked him if I overheard the baggage handler who mentioned the UFO correctly. He put his finger to his mouth to signal me to keep my questions to myself. Later that evening, I saw Joseph seated alone in the motel restaurant. I approached, and he stood, inviting me to join him. When I explained that I collected stories about UFOs and his conversation had piqued my interest, he leaned back in his chair and looked at me pensively. After a little encouragement and assurances, he agreed to tell his story.

"Before I tell you my story, I want you to know that I'm taking a chance on you. I'm willing to do it since you're helping my people obtain federal funds to help the youth on the reservation. But you must promise on your honor that you will never reveal my name, my airline, or the reservation by name. I've worked too hard to be a pilot to have it taken away from me because I encountered a UFO. It doesn't matter that every pilot has seen UFOs. It is expected that none of us talk about it."

"I understand and you have my word."

"I believe many abductees remember what occurred to them. The aliens don't seem to mind that. After all, who is going to pay attention to their story?"

"How many times have you seen a UFO?" I asked.

"Many times. When I was a pilot in the Persian Gulf, UFOs tracked me several times."

"How long have you been a pilot?"

"If the Air Force counts, fourteen years. I like flying small jets. I hope one day to have my own plane and shuttle people directly to the reservation. I'm just waiting for the tribe to build a small runway."

"Can you tell me about the UFO I overheard you talking about with the airport baggage handler?"

"Tonight, when you overheard my conversation with the baggage handler, we were not casually discussing UFOs. A report alerted the ground control that a UFO appeared on radar and was headed in the direction of our flight pattern. The military pilots from the nearby Air Force base were on alert. The baggage handler told me about it when we landed."

"Interesting. Is that the reason our plane was diverted?" I asked.

"No, it really was the weather." He smiled and turned his attention to the menu. Joseph was not particularly a handsome man. He probably stood about five feet nine. A gold band on his ring finger announced his marital status. His black, military-style haircut showed signs of gray at the temple. I estimated he was in his early forties. His smile revealed dimples on both cheeks, which were diminished because of the scars of acne on his face.

"I would love to hear about your actual encounter with the star travelers."

"I'm not sure where to begin," he said.

"Just start at the beginning."

"One night after I had been stateside for about six weeks, I decided to drive home to the reservation. I learned about the opening at an airline from a pilot friend of mine. It was near my home. He told me the airline had a reputation of hiring veterans. My wife and I decided to make a change. Our kids were in college, and I just wanted a new beginning. At the time, we were living in Alabama. I decided to drive home and set up things, get a house and hopefully a job. I drove almost non-stop across country, sleeping in rest stops a few hours and then getting back on the road."

He paused when the desk clerk handed him a message. He read it and then turned his attention back to me. "It looks like the storm will move out by the morning. We'll leave about 8:00 a.m."

"That's good news."

"Hopefully the runway will be cleared in time for the departure." He tipped his coffee cup and looked in it as though willing it to be full before calling for another refill. "Now, where was I?"

"You were telling me about your non-stop trip across America," I said.

"I was about fifty miles from Williston, North Dakota."

"I'm familiar with that area," I said. "It's fairly desolate."

He nodded. "I was on an isolated stretch of road. Suddenly I saw a huge orange globe on the highway ahead. I slowed. It looked like a huge ball of fire, perfectly round. The brightness was blinding. I pulled my car over to the edge of the highway and got out, trying to figure out what was going on. Without warning, two figures approached out of the light. I retreated toward my car, but as I reached for the door handle, I realized I couldn't move.

Then, all at once, I was airborne, literally floating through the air. The next thing I know, I was inside a flying saucer, an honest to God flying saucer."

He sat back in the booth and hugged himself as though he still could not believe it. "I was exhilarated. I wasn't afraid at all. I wanted to scour the craft and find out how it flew and meet the pilot."

"Can you describe the figures who took you onboard the craft?"

"They were taller than me by about three or four inches. Close to six feet, I'd say. They were hairless creatures but looked human, but I think that was solely for my comfort. They had no eyebrows or eyelashes. Their heads were rounder and slightly larger than humans. Their upper body was larger than their lower body making them appear as though they might topple over. They had large, round black eyes, bigger than human eyes, small noses and a mouth, but no lips. They didn't walk but floated everywhere."

"Do you think your abduction was random?" I asked.

"From the beginning there was no question but that my abduction was not random. They made it clear that they were interested in human pilots."

"Did they tell you why?"

"At first I thought they were trying to determine the mindset of a combat pilot. What made us so different that we could bomb and not suffer from remorse? They asked me, I should say grilled me, about my job and the military in general."

"Did they orally talk to you?" I asked.

"No. They communicated only telepathically, but I understood them. Oral communication meant nothing to them. It was all done with the mind. I couldn't help but question as to whether the human race is headed in that direction with all the technology. Why talk? Just think about it. It's easier. You don't have to waste time on choosing the right word." He paused and shook his head as if in disbelief of the possibilities.

"Were you able to witness any of their advanced technology?"

"I asked if they'd show me their ship. They agreed to show

me parts of it but denied me the right to see their control area. They said that the ship was controlled by thoughts. They indicated they had mastered the power of thought and were able to plot a destination or course and think about it and they would appear at that location. This kind of travel was incomprehensible to me."

"What did they allow you to see?" I asked.

"I saw a huge laboratory with perhaps a hundred patients but not all were human. Those that were human appeared to originate from all over the world. When I questioned them about the reason for the abductions, they simply replied it was clinical. They studied their abductees as scientists."

"So they regarded humans as lab rats."

"Exactly. Humans meant nothing to them. They did say that humans were only a small part of their program. They chose other 'intelligent' or dominant life forms on worlds throughout the galaxy. It was all part of their research. They considered themselves superior to other species in the universe and exploited their superior knowledge and technology."

"Did they tell you how they selected the individuals for participation in their research?"

"They preferred rural areas where they were unlikely to be detected. They wanted no witnesses to their perverse activities. They admitted that they try to block all knowledge of the abduction, but that it didn't always work. Humans were evolving, and for some their brains were less susceptible to suggestions. For others, it only lasted a short time. They abducted both skeptics and believers and examined them for brain differences. Occupation or educational level was also not a factor. If a person did remember the abduction, they didn't view them as a threat to their operation since most people on Earth were not strong believers in abduction."

"Why did they want you, a pilot? Did they ever reveal their interest in you?" I asked.

"They were interested in me for two reasons. First, as I mentioned, they were interested in what they called the 'psychological conditioning' of pilots that allowed us to bomb without remorse. Secondly, they led me to an area that was like a huge hanger. Inside were small planes from all over the world. There were military planes, private jets, crop dusters, seaplanes. It was like museum. Despite their 'superior intelligence' in the universe, they did not understand the mechanics of the plane or how to repair them."

"Did they tell you why they needed this information?"

"Only that it would allow them to use our own planes to interact with Earth without raising suspicion from the population."

"Did they explain what they meant?"

"I tried to get more information, but they ignored my questions."

"Did they perform any medical procedures on you?" I asked.

"No physical experimentation, but they tried to take my mind I think. They put me in a cylinder and attached a metal helmet to my head, but I remembered from my military training to use my mind to subvert the enemy should I be captured. I used that technique and it seemed to frustrate them. They were interested in my thought processes. They were also curious about emotions; they seemed to have none. Even in their communication, there was no variance in their speech. A question sounded the same as a statement."

"Can you tell me the techniques you used?"

"I really can't do that. It would be giving up military secrets, so let's just leave it at that."

"How long did they keep you onboard?" I asked.

"A few hours, but it seemed longer. There were so many questions I wanted answered, and I tried using a strategy of giving information only if they gave me information in return. They caught on quickly to this tactic, and when I delayed in answering them, they used pain."

He paused and looked around the room. He tapped the table nervously and then leaned closer. "Have you ever drunk a Slurpee too fast and had a brain freeze?"

I nodded.

"That's what they can do with a thought. The pain becomes so excruciating that you tell them what they want to know."

"Did you see them conducting experiments?"

"In the laboratory. I saw surgeries being performed where brains were exposed. I saw humans connected to machines. I saw and heard the screams of resisters. I voiced my disgust, and they hurried me out of the lab."

"Do you have any idea what they were doing?"

"They told me they were healing those with diseases. I don't know if it was true. Maybe they said it to lessen the horror I felt."

"Did you see anything else?"

"No. They were selective in their tour. When they released me, they said they would be back. That was three years ago, and so far I haven't seen them."

"How do you feel about that?"

"Relieved, but at the same time disappointed."

"Can you explain?"

"I think they're evil, but I think that the more we learn about them, the more we are prepared to deal with them."

"Have you ever thought about writing your story?" I asked.

"Maybe I'll go public on my deathbed," he said, laughing. "I'm not interested in drawing attention to myself. I don't talk with anyone about my experience. I'm a small-town pilot. I live in small, reservation town. I don't want people thinking I'm a nut case."

"But your people have a history that dates back to the beginning of time about Star People. I have heard legends of what appears to be abduction," I said.

"I know. My grandpa told me those legends too, but I'm not sure people want a pilot who sees UFOs."

"With your permission, I want to tell your story, but I will not use your real name or location."

"Permission granted." He looked at his watch and slid out of the booth. "I'd better get some rest. Five o'clock comes early, and I have to be at the airport by 6 a.m. if we're scheduled to depart on time. I'll see you in the morning."

I see Joseph occasionally. Since I retired, I do not travel as much as I once did. On my last trip aboard the airline, I met Joseph's wife, Melinda, who spoke glowingly of her husband and his commitment to bringing his tribe into the technological age.

14. LILY'S STORY: TURQUOISE STONES AND MIRACLE HANDS

Lily owned a small business on the reservation, specializing in handmade objects from registered American Indian artists. Located in an area where tourists often visited, her business had grown from a one-room store forty years ago to a large 10,000-square-foot establishment with thirty-five full-time employees, all American Indians. As a lover of turquoise jewelry, I often stopped in her shop for the latest designs from contemporary artists. Lily set aside pieces that she thought might interest me. We often talked about the origin of the turquoise, the artist, and the history behind a particular piece of jewelry. It was on one such stopover that she showed me a bracelet of a single turquoise stone and explained that she had personally found the unique stone and had hired an artist to create the bracelet. When she told me the origin of the stone, I was not prepared for her revelation.

Lily and I planned to go to Las Vegas to take in the Celine Dion concert at Caesar's Palace. Both of us were fans and decided a weekend in sin city was what both of us needed. On Sunday, Lily insisted we drive to Tonopah, Nevada. "Why are we going to Tonopah?" I asked as we drove down the highway.

"Do you still collect stories about UFOs?" Lily asked as we drove down the highway headed for Tonopah.

"I do. Not as much as I'd like. I limit my travel now to about two trips a year. The older I get, the more I treasure my time at home."

"I hear you. I'm the same way," she said as I passed an elderly man driving forty on the Interstate. "Yet I have to admit, it sure was fun to meet up with you and go to the concert. In my younger days,

I used to spend every weekend digging for turquoise. In the old days, my favorite place was the hills around Tonopah. They were riddled with turquoise, and on occasion I would find a priceless gem. My dad was a jeweler, and I used to hunt turquoise stones for him. My dream back then was to have a turquoise mine in the Tonopah area. But before I was old enough, the Ottenson's moved in and bought up most of the mining rights. Now he has mining tours at a hundred dollars a person where you can dig for turquoise and all the other tourist trappings. That's where all the Royston turquoise is found."

"Are we going to a turquoise mine?"

"Not exactly. We'll stop in Tonopah and stay the night. I made reservations at the Best Western. I just have something special I want to show you."

The next morning, we were up early and headed north toward the reservation. After about forty-five minutes into the trip, Lily pointed to the right. "Pull over here. We need to take this road about a mile."

"Is this a road?" I asked. It appeared to be a one-lane, dirt path.

"It is to me. Not well-traveled, but it's a road. We need to go just a little ways. I'm taking you to my favorite turquoise spot."

"Do you mean where you hunted turquoise as a child?" I asked.

"I still dig for turquoise here. Just not as often as when I was a teenager."

I slowed and looked at the huge rut in the road, making sure I straddled it.

"Let's park over there." Lily pointed to a spot big enough for a vehicle. I pulled over.

"Come, I want to show you something," she said.

I got out of the car and followed as she hiked up the side of a hill. We climbed no more than fifty feet before she sat down.

"I was sitting in this area," she said, looking around. "I was tired from digging and taking a short rest. Over there is where I first saw it."

"Saw what?"

"The UFO. I wanted you to see the spot. That's why I brought you here."

"What were they doing?"

"I watched for maybe five minutes, and they were just hovering there. No sound, no movement, just like they were suspended from invisible ropes from the sky."

"How big was it?"

"My best estimation was maybe fifty feet around and thirty feet high. It wasn't gigantic by any means. It was a dark gray color. There weren't any windows. Not an artistic design. It could easily be described as two pasta bowls sealed together, only they'd have to be large. But you get the message. I'm talking about the shape. As I sat watching the craft, a man approached me."

"A man? Do you mean someone else saw it?"

"No, I mean a man from the spaceship. Well, I have to admit I thought it was a human man at first. He looked like a man. He wore a dark brown jumpsuit and brown boots. When I looked up at him—remember I am sitting, the sun reflected in my eyes—I couldn't make out much about his face. He was about six feet tall. He had very long hands and fingers."

"Did you talk with him? I asked.

"Oh, yes. I told him I was looking for turquoise and that I had been coming here since I was a teenager. In fact, I was just rambling on about my life's history to this stranger. I don't know why I talked so much. I told him I owned a shop and where it was located. I told him about my ex-husband and my kids. I just went on and on."

"What was he doing while you were talking?"

"He seemed to be listening. And then, when I stopped and he didn't say anything, I talked about my life again until there was nothing more to tell. Then I fell silent again, waiting for him to say something. By now, I thought he might be a pervert, and I was organizing in my mind how I might escape when he told me not to be afraid. Then I told him about my hunt for the perfect turquoise stone over the years. I explained that natural turquoise stones suitable for jewelry were hard to find. I told him that most turquoise is treated to alter its color with dyes and to stabilize it with various chemicals intended to increase its hardness or luster. He seemed interested in what I was saying and asked me questions about turquoise."

"Was the stranger speaking orally to you?"

"At the time, I thought so, but later I discovered he was using mind-reading as a way to communicate. He would think a question. I would think an answer."

"What is the UFO doing while you are talking with him?"

"It was still hovering right there," she said pointing. "It didn't move."

"Did you ask him about it?"

"No. It didn't seem important when he arrived. It was like the UFO was a normal event. He didn't mention it either."

"After a couple of minutes, he asked me to follow him. We walked east around the side of the mountain, and he kneeled and picked up two large rocks. He held them, one in each hand. I saw each hand glow, and when he handed the stones to me, they were the most perfect turquoise gemstones I had ever seen. It was amazing."

"What did you do after you saw the gemstone?"

"I asked him how he did it, but he did not reply. Instead he walked down the hill, and I swear he walked under the UFO and a beam fell on him just as he disappeared. I had the stones made into two bracelets. I have them in the car. One is for you."

"But..."

"No buts. I want you to have it. It was made specifically for your wrist. I know how you have always been interested in UFO stories. Well, now you have one that is true, and you can wear a turquoise stone that was fashioned by a star man. And I swear to you—just as you and I are standing her—he was real and he existed. He came off a spaceship and he returned to a spaceship."

"Did you ever see a face?"

"No. His eyes were covered with huge goggles that wrapped

around his head, and I swear, too, he had no lips."

"When he handed you the stones, did you say anything to him?"

"I asked him how he transformed the turquoise in the large rock into a beautiful stone, and he said energy. When I questioned him about the energy, he said I possessed energy too, but didn't know how to use it."

"And?"

"I offered to return them to him, and he said they were for me."

"Do you think he was collecting turquoise?"

"No. I don't know what he was collecting, but he had a pouch about twelve inches by twelve hung across his chest and by his side. I know he collected something because the bag appeared full."

"What other stones are found in this area?"

"Nevada has all kinds of minerals. We produce more silver and gold than any state. There are many kinds of turquoise besides Royston. There's Apache Blue, Blue Ice, Blue Jay or Lander, Blue Goose, and Blue Moon. Then there is amethyst, opal, quartz, beryl, azurite, to name a few. But I can't imagine an alien wanting any of those unless they know a use for them that we do not know, although now that I think about it, he did seem to take an interest in quartz."

"Do you remember anything else?"

"Yeah. As I stood looking at the stones, he touched my back. I felt heat at first, and then it became hotter and hotter. He told me I would never have back pain again. He healed me."

"How did he do that?"

"With his miracle hands. The same hands he used to make the turquoise stones. He took away my pain."

"Anything else?"

"Yes. I need to show you something. A couple of weeks after I saw him and the UFO, I returned to the area searching for turquoise. Out of curiosity, I walked over the bank to look at the area where the UFO had been. And there, amongst all the weeds and cacti, was a barren circle. Come, I want to show you."

I tried to keep up with her as she excitedly chatted about the circle. When we arrived at the spot, I understood her animation. There was definitely a circle. Lily ran into the middle of it, held her hands upward, and called out: "Where are you star man?" but there was no reply.

"I come here as often as I can," Lily said. "I have so many questions and I want to ask him to teach me how he processed the turquoise with his hands. I want to learn."

We hardly talked on our way to the reservation, both of us deep in thought. I couldn't help but admire the beautiful, oversized stone on the bracelet around my wrist. Not only was it gorgeous, but it had been created by a star man.

I see Lily once or twice a year depending on how often I go south. The last time I saw her, she was thinking about retirement. We have been talking about going to Shania Twain's concert. If we make it, I am sure we will make the trip from Las Vegas to the reservation with a stopover in Tonopah. If we're lucky, we'll find the once-in-a-lifetime turquoise stone, but then I can't help but think: I already have one!

15. SMOKEY BEAR'S STORY: THE NIGHT THE RESERVATION ALMOST BURNED DOWN

Edwin was a member of the Rez Boy Hot Shots, an all-Indian, twenty-member firefighting team that specialized in traveling to remote locations to battle wildfires. He earned his name "Smokey Bear" from an event that happened when he first joined the Hot Shots. While on location, the team was ordered to evacuate due to the speed and direction of the fire. Upon regrouping to their fallback position, they discovered that their new recruit, Edwin, was missing. Just as the situation turned bleak and his chances of survival decreased with the ticking of the clock, Edwin came out of the fire carrying a badly burned bear cub. One of the firefighters yelled, "There's Smokey and his bear." From that time, Edwin was known as Smokey Bear.

Before I retired from Montana State University, I worked with a number of reservation school districts developing an At-Risk Response Team, which involved law enforcement, paramedics, firefighters, elders, psychologists, and teachers. It was a part of a safe-schools program established under the Bush presidency and proved to be an extremely successful project. Smokey was a member of the ten-member team organized on his reservation to serve youth at risk of dropping out of school or becoming involved in drugs and alcohol. Although he was the youngest member of the team, his enthusiasm and optimism guided the rest of the members. He was considered a desirable bachelor by the women on the reservation. When I first met him, his smile and humble manner made him stand out among others in the room.

After the meeting when each member had assigned duties to

accomplish, Smokey hung back and helped the school cafeteria staff clear the tables and empty the wastebaskets. As I carried the last wastebasket to the dumpster, Smokey ran ahead of me and offered to help. He paused in my path and looked at me. "I don't know how to say this," he said as he shuffled his feet and looked at the ground. It was the first time I had seen him almost afraid to speak up. I stood silently, giving him time to respond. Although he was over six feet tall and obviously in top shape from the muscles that bulged beneath his black t-shirt, he looked like a boy who had been called to the principal's office.

"Everyone knows you collect UFO stories," he blurted out.

I nodded.

"I know a true UFO story if you would like to hear it. I've never told anyone about it because it is so weird no one would believe it, but I swear to you, it's the truth."

"I'm not going to think it's weird. That's why I collect stories: to give individuals a chance to talk about what happened to them. I would be honored to hear your story."

He looked at me and smiled. "You'll keep it a secret, right?"

"You have my word." He reached out his hand and we shook. My word was my bond and he knew it.

"Do you have to be anywhere right now?" he asked.

"No, it's six o'clock. I have no appointments this evening."

"Good. We have plenty of time, because if it's okay with you, I want you to take a drive with me."

I nodded, indicating it was okay.

"Now, don't move. I'll get my truck and pick you up."

Five minutes later, Smokey drove up in a black Toyota Tundra. I climbed in, and we took the two-lane highway headed south. About twenty miles from town, he took a side road and headed north on a neglected gravel road. Soon the gravel road ended, and we bumped along a rutted, washed out, overgrown road, which reminded me of a cow path. Suddenly the landscape took a different turn, and I was looking at blackened surroundings. Black, burned stubs of trees dotted the landscape.

"This fire happened a year ago," Smokey said. "The elders call it the 'dead place.' No one comes here anymore, but before the fire, it was a popular hunting ground. It took us three weeks to get it under control and another to squelch all the trees burning underground."

"I didn't know trees burned underground."

"When a fire is really fierce, the roots continue to burn even though the above part is put out. It can go on for days and can actually reignite fires if there is anything to burn."

"I learned something today. I didn't know about burning roots."

"There is something else," he said. "The fire was caused by a UFO."

He put his truck in four-wheel drive and headed west. We climbed a small hill, dodging burned timbers all the way. When we reached the top, he parked the truck and pointed out the path the fire took.

"Ben Old Eagle lived in that house on that ridge. You can see the roof." I followed his finger that was pointing to the north. "The fire started about midnight. I was at home at the time. Ben—he was my uncle—called me and said a ball of fire flew south over his house. He was worried about prairie fires. The reservation land was parched. No rain all summer."

"Did you go to Ben's place?"

"I did."

"What did you see?"

"By the time I got there, Ben's fear was real. A fire had already started. I called the Hot Shots. I asked them to call the police to warn residents in the area."

"By the looks of it, the fire would not be easy to put out. It wasn't an ordinary fire by any means. It was definitely fueled by something we had never encountered."

"The UFO?"

He nodded.

"After I alerted the Hot Shots, I suited up," said Edwin. He kept his gear in his truck at all times for emergencies. "Uncle Ben and I got in my pickup and headed out. We traced the path of the fire. It was about a half-mile at that time. As we came to a dead end—I assumed it was the place where the fireball met the earth— we saw a circular craft engulfed in flames. The fire was so hot that I had to back up the pickup to get to a safe distance. If you look at the hood of my pickup, you can see the blistered paint. It was from the heat we encountered."

"Can you tell me more about the circular craft?" I asked.

"It was large, about fifty feet in circumference. I will take you to the site where it happened. The spot where it came to a stop is still visible."

We returned to the pickup and continued our journey. I sat in silence as I looked at the results of the devastating fire. In another thirty minutes or so, we arrived at the area where he saw the UFO. There was no question that something unusual had occurred at this spot. A huge, blackened circle was visible. There were no trees or evidence that life had ever existed in this area.

"This is where the craft came to a stop. Uncle and I watched as the fire, which was so intense, destroy it. It melted before our eyes. We couldn't believe it."

"Were there any remains of the ship?"

"Before Uncle and I could do anything, we spotted several balls of light circling above the downed craft. We saw several beams of light come out of the sky from the balls of light and center on the craft engulfed in flames."

"What were they doing?"

"I believe they were recovering the bodies of the occupants inside the craft."

"Why would you think that?"

"As Uncle and I sat there, we saw one of the occupants fleeing the fire. He ran toward our pickup, his arms upraised with his legs on fire. Before I had a chance to respond, the figure suddenly began to rotate and became a brilliant ball of light. As I was trying to make sense of what I had seen, a beam of light swooped up the ball of light and it disappeared."

"After the fire cleared, were there any remnants of the spacecraft?" I asked.

"Nothing. In fact, an investigation into the cause of the fire resulted in an 'undetermined' cause. The investigation team said it was an unexplainable combustion, which could have been caused by intense lighting."

"Have you ever told anyone this story."

"We agreed that we would not tell anyone the story. We didn't want government men on the reservation and, worst yet, tons of reporters. We didn't want to bring attention to ourselves."

He paused and walked to the back of the pickup, opened a cooler in the back, and offered me a bottle of water. "Ben died last year, and now that he's gone. I think it's okay that I share this event with you. You can write about it, talk about it, but just keep this location and me away from the news."

"You can count on it."

"The night still haunts me. The image of the Star Man fleeing the fire and running toward us for safety is stamped on my brain. But at night I'm haunted by the balls of light. Uncle called this place the sacred place. The elders call it the dead place. But I know it is the place where a UFO crashed and the survivors lived to fly the heavens again."

"So now that time has passed, what do you think about what happened that night?"

"I've learned a lot about space travel. I've been reading books about space travel and astronomy. I'm what the elders call a Space Age Indian. My heart is in the stars, but my feet are on Earth. Someday, I believe I will go there."

"What do you mean when you call yourself a Space Age Indian?" I asked.

"Well, that's how I think of myself. If the aliens ever came back, I would go with them into space. I study a lot of things to make myself useful. I've learned about all kinds of engines. I have studied and practiced gardening. I read everything I can about space and astronomy. I go online and visit a number of astronomy sites. I chat with others with similar interests. I'm ready to go to the stars."

I continued to see Smokey over the next six years while I was involved in the Safe Schools Project. He is still on his quest to learn all he can learn about space. On two other occasions, Smokey and I have returned to the site of the UFO crash. The most amazing thing about the area is that all around the site wildflowers grow, buffalo grass sways in the wind, and young trees about a foot tall are making a comeback. However, the area where Smokey saw the UFO ablaze remains darkened and lifeless, a testament to what happened on the night that Smokey calls a time when the reservation almost burned down.

16. CISCO'S STORY:
THE ELECTRIFIED MAN

I met Cisco one night at a community graduation party. He introduced himself as the father of Dakota Blue, the valedictorian of the graduating students. As I walked over to the refreshment stand, he followed me. When there was no one else around, he explained that he had an encounter with a UFO and would like to share his story with me. We agreed to meet at a restaurant off the reservation at 7 p.m. the next evening.

I arrived at the restaurant ten minutes before our appointed meeting and chose a seat far removed from other diners. As I looked around the dining area, the majority of the customers appeared to be locals. They yelled across tables about weather and cattle prices, greeted each other as old friends when they entered, and called the employees by their first names. When Cisco entered the reception area, everyone stopped talking, looked in his direction, and whispered to each other as he followed the hostess to the back table where I was waiting. At well over six-feet tall with the broad shoulders of an athlete, he was a striking figure. He was dressed in a plaid shirt and jeans with a turquoise nugget bolo tie and a matching ring on his finger.

"Do you know the people in this restaurant?" I asked as he seated himself, removed his cowboy hat, and placed it on the vacant chair beside him.

"Maybe I should say, they know me, but I don't know them." He picked up the menu and then set it aside. "I'm an Indian and this is a border town. They hate Indians here. They just want our money. The town would fold without reservation money, but that doesn't stop their racism. They especially don't like Indians who can eat in the same place they do."

I nodded. I knew he was speaking the truth. I had seen the same reaction in border towns throughout the west. South Dakota, North Dakota, Montana, Wyoming—they were all the same.

"Do you know who the Cisco Kid is?" he asked, as he placed the menu on the side of the table.

"Do you mean O'Henry's fictional character of TV and comic books?" I responded.

"The same," he said, smiling. "My dad was a big fan of Cisco Kid. When I was born, he named me after that character. So when I go about my business, I always remember that the Cisco Kid never let prejudice or the reaction of others impact the way he behaved."

"So why do you come here?" I asked. "Wouldn't it be easier to go to an Indian-friendly restaurant?"

"Because I have to set an example for my son. He's going to face adversity in life. People are going to judge him for the color of his skin, his last name, being an Indian. I want him to know that he's worthy. That it doesn't matter what others think as long as he's a good person. He's a good boy. I know he'll be a good man, but I have to teach him that life is not easy."

"If you want my opinion," I said, "I think you've done a good job. I heard Dakota has been accepted at the university with a full scholarship."

"He wants to go to medical school after he finishes his bachelor's. He's studying biomedical sciences, which should give him a leg up on a good school. I will do whatever it takes to help him. If he chooses medical school, I will help him all I can."

He paused as the waiter brought our food.

"So tell me," I said once the waiter had left, "you said you had a story to tell. Where would you like to begin?"

"I'm an electrician by trade. I learned it in the Army, and when I got out, I passed the state exams to become licensed. I have my own business and have six other men who work for me. Because

I'm an Indian business, I'm frequently called by other tribes to troubleshoot problems, train their electricians, and so on. I'm a single dad, so I have really been selective over the years about what I do. In the summers, when Dakota is out of school, I take him with me. It is a special time for the two of us."

"Was it on another reservation where you had your encounter?" I asked.

He nodded, and I watched as he cut his steak into small bite-size pieces.

"It was down South," he began. "It was close to Christmas time when I got a call. There was a terrible storm, and most of the reservation was in the dark. Dakota was still in school, but I knew the tribe was really in need of my help. Cattle and sheep were dying, people were starving, and three people had died of exposure, but I didn't want to leave Dakota over the holidays. I met with Dakota's teachers, and they released him early, and we set out for a three-week working holiday."

"How old was Dakota at that time?"

"He was a freshman. He's seventeen now, so that would have made him thirteen. He was excited about going. We planned for a three-day driving trip, but it took us nearly five days because of the snow. By the time we arrived, food was being airlifted to remote areas, but the snowdrifts were so high people were still stranded. Many had not had electricity for two weeks, and the tribal electricians, who were working eighteen-hour shifts, had been unable to locate the source of the problem."

"Was it on the reservation that you had your encounter?" I asked.

"I have to tell this story in my own time."

He signaled the waiter who appeared at our table almost at once. "Please bring us some coffee," he said, "and two orders of your huckleberry cheesecake for desert." When I tried to resist the order, he held up his hand and said, "If you don't eat it, I will. They make their cheesecake with wild huckleberries. It's the best."

"Please, continue your story," I said.

"When I arrived at the tribal headquarters, the chairman had set up a makeshift apartment for us at the tribal office. There was no motel space available. I spent the first day going over the schematics of the electrical service. By the next morning, I had a good idea of the areas to check. The chairman ordered a snowplow to accompany me, and we set out. For two days, we traveled the backroads. He plowed, and I followed. Each time we dug out one site, I sent him to another to save time. It was tedious going. Sometimes we came up against twenty-to-thirty-foot drifts. I began to wonder if we would ever be able to complete the job."

He paused, took a drink of his coffee and ate a bite of his cheesecake. He waited for me to take a bite. When a smile crossed my face, he had a look of someone who had just won a prize. "I told you it was the best cheesecake ever," he said.

I nodded and took another bite savoring it. "Please continue," I said.

"On our fifth day on the reservation, it was Christmas Eve. It was getting late, and the snowplow driver wanted to head back to his family. I told him to go ahead. I would be along in a half hour or so. After he left, the enormity of the silence around me felt ominous. It's difficult to explain. It was dark and cold. The sun had been coming out during the day, and now everything was starting to freeze. I opened up the electrical junction, and I thought I'd discovered the source of the problem. Just as I completed the job, I saw a light in the distance. At first, I thought it was the plow, but as it came closer, I knew it was no truck."

"Can you describe what you saw?"

"It appeared as two lights at first, but as it got closer, I saw that it was only one. Then I saw it. It was definitely some kind of a flying craft. I thought it might be a helicopter bringing in food, but there was no sound. It never occurred to me it was a spacecraft. I climbed into my pickup and tried to start the engine, as it came closer and closer. I have to admit, I was afraid it was going to crash. I wondered what a flying craft would be doing on this remote section of the reservation. And that's when it happened."

He finished off his cheesecake and picked up his coffee mug. "What happened?" I asked.

"The craft hovered over the power line. It was a round, circular object about forty or fifty feet in diameter. I saw it steal electricity from the lines. It was like jagged lightening going from the lines to the craft. I jumped out of my pickup to get a better look."

"But you said you were afraid. When did you change your mind?"

"I was still afraid, but I couldn't help myself. This was the most amazing thing I had ever seen. As the electricity entered the craft, a rosy glow emitted from the craft. I heard a hum like a motor running very softly. I stood there peering up at the craft wondering if they were going to destroy my work, when all of a sudden, they seemed to know of my existence. I returned to the pickup and locked the doors. That's when they moved from the power line and gently landed in front of my pickup, blocking my way."

"Did you see any occupants of the craft?" I asked.

"Only one, but he almost gave me a heart attack. I was totally unprepared for it. I had no way of defending myself. I thought about my son. He would be waiting for me. I had promised to have Christmas Eve dinner with him. Suddenly, a panel slid back from the craft and a being came toward me. He was curious about my presence in this isolated spot. He kept asking me what I was doing."

"Did you get a good look at him?"

"Not a good look at his face. He was humanoid in appearance but this glowing, shimmering light like electricity encompassed his entire body. I could tell he had a human form, but the light was so bright that I could not look directly at him. I kept wondering if this was a secret government project. I yelled at him and asked who he was."

"Did he reply?"

"He said he came from out there and that he would be gone soon. I'd seen them take the electricity and figured he was capable of most anything."

"Was he talking to you orally?" I asked.

"I don't know. I talked to him orally. When I explained I was repairing the electricity so people would have light, he told me he knew where the major problem was, and it was not the junction where I was working. He said there was another junction that was critical to all the electricity on the reservation. He offered to take me there and help."

"How was he going to get you there?"

"That was the question I asked. The area he was speaking about was still obstructed by tons of snow. The snowplow driver expected it would take several days to clear the road. I had concentrated instead on the other potential problem areas, thinking it might be possible to restore power at least to a few hundred families. He said I could restore the power within an hour or so with his help."

"Did you decide to take the Star Man up on his offer?" I asked.

"I did. I walked inside an area only lighted by his appearance. The hair all over my body stood up as though electrified. Within a minute, we were hovering over the junction. I unscrewed the panel cover and the problem was obvious. It had never been below freezing on the reservation prior to this freakish snowstorm, and the junction box was frozen. As I tried to decide how to melt the frozen connections without causing a major shutdown of the whole grid, the star traveler used his hands to melt the connections and dry them. Afterwards, we rechecked everything. When I called the tribal office, they were celebrating. The electrical grid was restored throughout the reservation. I thanked the visitor. On the return to my pickup, I mentioned that I had a two-hour drive ahead of me, and he said he would take care of that."

"How did he do that?"

"The next thing I know I'm on the outskirts of the town in my pickup headed for the tribal office. My son and I had Christmas Eve dinner together."

"So you restored the power throughout the reservation," I said.

"The entire reservation. Calls were coming in to the tribal office thanking the tribal chairman. He was excited. He knew that with the upcoming election, he would definitely be re-elected. He gave me a thousand-dollar bonus on top of my pay, which I put in Dakota's college savings account."

"So now that three years have passed, would you say that your encounter changed your life?"

"The Star Man taught me that there are other beings in the universe and that he came from a civilization where people helped each other. Most people on the reservation are that way. They look out for each other. He showed me it's the same way in space."

I did not see Cisco again until several months later, and we do keep in touch when I visit the reservation. He always insists on taking me out to eat steak and huckleberry cheesecake. Dakota is making perfect grades in college but enjoys coming home each summer and helping his father in his electrical business. He still plans to be a doctor. Cisco spends more time consulting with other tribes now that his son is away at school. He says he hopes to see the Star Man again. He has made a list of questions to ask him if he does return, but so far, he has not visited him again.

17. RAIN'S STORY: HE WAS AGELESS

Rain was a single mother of two who managed to complete a PhD in psychiatry at a prestigious university. After four years as a practitioner, she took a job as assistant professor at her alma mater. While she lived in the city, Rain maintained close ties with her home reservation and took advantage of every opportunity to visit her mother and grandmother. Proud of her strong, matriarchal family, Rain instilled the same independence in her daughters. While she valued the traditional values of her people and practiced them in her daily life, Rain had a secret. That secret inspired her to contact me.

I met Rain at the National Association of Bilingual Education convention in Phoenix, Arizona. Accompanied by twin daughters who were the image of her mother, Rain asked if she could meet me privately after conference hours. We agreed to meet in her suite after dinner.

"Thank you for coming," she said as she reached for my arm and pulled me inside her sitting room. "We only have a couple of hours before the girls will be back. They went to the movies across the street with some friends. I don't want them to know about this, but I had to tell someone. A psychiatrist needing a psychologist. Go figure." She laughed uncomfortably and picked up a pack of cigarettes. "I hope you don't mind," she said. "I smoke when I'm nervous."

"There's no need to be nervous," I told her. "If you want to tell me your story, I'm here to listen."

She lit the cigarette and took the chair across from me. She was a petite woman with long, black straight hair. Dressed in sweat pants and a t-shirt, she could have passed for one of her teenage daughters. Although she wore too much red lipstick and eye shadow, her soft features and flawless skin revealed a natural beauty.

"I first met the star people when I was twenty years old. I had been away at college and came home for summer break. My mom and grandma had a small place in the country: just five acres and a Mutual Help Home that they helped build themselves. There was tribal land around our property so it seemed as though the whole world was at my fingertips. My mom and grandma both worked for the tribe. I had a horse, Starlight, that I raised from a colt. They took care of her when I was away. We had a few chickens and a garden. Just a regular family. I looked forward to my summers in the country. Horseback riding was my passion, and I loved to take Starlight on all-day rides across tribal land."

"Did you have your encounter on one of those trips?" I asked.

She nodded and reached for another cigarette. She walked to the refrigerator. "Would you like a drink?" I accepted one of two Diet Cokes she held in her hand.

"I often road north, taking a familiar path that allowed me to circle around and come in from the south along the river below our house. I often stopped, enjoyed the scenery, had my lunch by the river, and allowed Starlight to drink and graze. It was on one such ride that I first met the Star Men."

"Can you tell me about the meeting?"

"I came up over a hill and looked down toward the valley. I saw a circular craft about sixty feet in circumference resting in the valley below. I was astonished, bewildered, and curious—all at the same time. It didn't register with me that I was seeing a flying saucer. I pushed Starlight downhill slowly as I surveyed the surroundings. When we got half way down the hill, Starlight became anxious and balked. He had always been obedient to my directions, but this time he stood steadfast. He refused to move. I jumped down from the saddle, and he bolted and ran back up the mountain. I knew there was no use in trying to catch him. He was headed for home."

"What did you do?"

"I continued my descent. I had come this far and I wasn't going to climb back up the hill. My plan was to reach the river and follow it until I was home. In the meantime, I planned to investigate the object in the valley below. As I approached it, maybe about twenty feet from it, I smelled something unusual. I tried to stifle my cough, but the odor irritated my lungs and I began coughing violently. I covered my mouth and nose, and decided I'd better get away from the object when suddenly I came face to face with a Star Man. At the same time, I became dizzy and blacked out." She paused, paced the floor, and lit another cigarette. She took a sip of her Coke and looked at me.

"What happened next?"

"I don't know. The next thing I remember is that I'm inside the spacecraft. I'm lying on a metal table and I'm no longer dizzy or coughing. I try to sit up but I can't. It's like my body is stuck to the table. I scream as loud as I can. I don't know why. I knew no one was coming for me. I thought of my mother and grandmother. They would never know what happened to me."

"You said you came face to face with a Star Man. How long did he keep you in the room?"

"I'm really not sure. When a door opened and he entered the room, I could suddenly move. I sat up and looked at him. He looked like an ordinary human. He was about five-foot-ten. He wore a blue one-piece outfit that extended over his feet and head. He told me I had nothing to fear from him. I believed him. I felt nothing but love and caring from him. He asked me to stand, and he took me by the arm and guided me to an area that he said was the guidance system. I asked him if he was alone, and he said there were two others. The ship had mechanical problems, and they were forced to land. He said there were minerals here that could serve as a temporary repair. I don't remember the name of the minerals. I have racked my brain trying to remember but nothing comes. There is no mineral I know of that would assist in space travel in that area, but I'm not a geologist or an engineer."

"Did you see the others?"

"No. Only him."

"Are you sure he was human?"

"As human as you or me."

"Did he look like an Indian?"

"His skin was dark. His eyes were black. I never saw his hair; it was under a cap like a hood but form-fitting."

"How did he speak to you?"

"He spoke English."

"Did he speak orally?"

"I'm not sure. I remember I felt love from him, but the love of a brother or father."

"Did you learn anything about why he was traveling the universe?"

"That's the strangest part of all. He said that throughout history his people had visited earth. In the early days of Earth's history, they interacted with humans and even worked with them. But today it is different. With our advanced technology, the risk of interacting with humans has taken on a greater risk and is forbidden by his people. He told me I should never talk about our meeting and that it should be a secret between us. He said knowledge of our contact would not turn out well for me."

"So why are you telling your story now?"

"I'm compelled to tell it. I feel like I have to tell someone to keep my sanity."

"I don't understand."

"Last year, I took the summer off. I hadn't had time off since I got my PhD. I took my girls, who would be graduating high school the next year, to the reservation to spend the summer with Mom. Although we often visited her throughout the year, I hadn't spent the summer there in many years. Starlight was still there. He was much older, but as soon as he saw me I knew he wanted to go for one of our rides. One Sunday afternoon, Mom took the girls to church and then planned to go to a picnic; I saddled him and took our usual path. Although he moved slower, we made our way to the site of the spaceship landing. As we came up over the hill, I saw it in the valley below."

"The spacecraft?"

She nodded. She lit another cigarette and looked at me. "I'm sorry I'm smoking so much."

"It's okay. Please go on with your story."

"Like the time twenty years earlier, I got off Starlight and dropped his reins. This time, Starlight did not desert me. He stood at the top of the hill as though he was observing. When we reached the valley bed, I called out to the Star Man and he appeared in an instant."

"Where was he?"

"I'm not sure. Anyway, he greeted me as an old friend. He reached out and touched Starlight, who seemed to be comfortable in his presence."

"Did you go inside the craft again?"

"Not this time. We walked along the river. We sat on a boulder that jutted over the water. The Star Man told me that since our first meeting he had returned to the same spot every year on the date of our meeting in hopes of seeing me again."

"Did he tell you why he returned?"

"He said he came to ask me to go away with him. He had been waiting for me to return to this spot."

"To go away with him? Where?"

"To his world." She looked at her watch. "I told him that I was a mother of two daughters and I could not go away with him. He encouraged me to bring them with me and move to his planet. I told him I had responsibilities and that my mother was getting older and needed me. He offered to take her, too."

"Why did he want to take you away?"

"He wasn't specific—only that life on Earth would become very difficult, and he was giving me a chance to have a new life."

"I told him it was impossible and that I would never leave Earth. It was strange. He showed no emotion, and yet I felt a love like I had never known. It was difficult to reject him. He got up, and I watched him go. For a long time, I sat there. I watched the spacecraft move upward, and within seconds it was gone. As it disappeared, I felt extremely sad. I knew I would never see him again."

"Have you?"

"No. I return every year, but he has not returned. I keep thinking he will have a change of heart, but I guess my rejection was considered final."

"Have you changed your mind?" I asked.

"Not really, but I can't help but think I missed the chance of a lifetime."

She sat down and stubbed out her cigarette. "That's my story."

"Anything else you remember?"

"Yes. In the twenty years that passed since I first saw him, he had not aged at all. He was not only kind, but he was ageless."

I keep in touch with Rain even though my days in academia are over. She has attained a full professorship at her university, and her daughters are now studying at a university out-of-state. Her mother passed two years ago, but Rain continues to return to the reservation during her summer breaks and waits for her Star Man. So far, he has not returned.

CONCLUSION

When I set out to write this book, I wanted to discover if those who had grown up in the Space Age had encounters that were significantly different from those who had little or no contact with computers, TV, the internet, or social media. Like other interviewees in my previous books, those who shared their accounts were not prompted to reveal their encounters in the hopes of celebrity or financial gain. They were often reluctant to share their story and did so only when assured of anonymity.

Like those who lived a more secluded life and out of range of the technological society, these interviewees presented a consistency of detail in their narratives and the extraordinary circumstances where these events occurred were similar to others and generated a sense of authenticity that cannot be found in fiction. While many of the accounts included descriptions of alien entities that have been detailed by others, the uniqueness of the encounters were different.

Perhaps the glowing exception emerged in the appearance of the Blue Men in war settings. While I have encountered many stories of the Blue Men from veterans, this group confided that the Blue Men spirited away fallen soldiers with the promise of a new life on another planet.

In spite of these differences, there was no evidence that the interviewees were influenced by pop culture. While differences were found, it appears as though the activities of the various Star People or alien entities have not changed significantly since the first abduction event. It does appear that some of their motives have evolved, but the main purposes of their visits have not changed. They are still using humans for procreation. Some are malevolent, but others are benevolent. Some appear to want to help the human race; others appear ambivalent toward humans and consider them nothing more than specimens to be studied. Some show an abundance of concern for humans through healings; while others appear to mock the pain of captives.

While the stories told in this book by individuals like you and me suggest that extraterrestrials visit this planet almost daily, we have no really hard evidence to prove that is the case. There have been no captured spaceships, no captured aliens, and nothing left by the aliens that would indicate they were from another world or possessed a highly advanced technology. But as a researcher and social scientist, I believe the stories in this book are genuine, legitimate, and indisputable. American Indians have always had a close relationship with the Star People, and those relationships have not faded with time but appear to be on the increase. However, one thing appears certain: the space travelers of today may not be the Star People of our grandfathers' day. Instead, it appears that in this great universe, more and more alien species have found a way to visit our Mother Earth and not all of them are here to watch over us.

ACKNOWLEDGEMENTS

When a book is completed it is a common practice to acknowledge those who helped in its creation. In a book such as this one, those who deserve recognition are honored by their omission. I am referring, in particular, to the men and women who told me their stories. As promised, I have maintained their anonymity, but that does not make their stories any less important. Their willingness to share their stories with me has made this book possible.

In addition, I offer my regards to all of those who supported me during my research. While acknowledging each of you personally might lead to the discovery of some of the individuals who told me their stories, you know who you are, and you know I will be forever grateful.

It has taken three years for this book to be completed. I owe my deepest gratitude to my editor, Patrick Huyghe, whose support for this work from the very beginning through its completion was unparalleled.

A special thanks goes to my husband, Kip, who nursed me back to health as I recuperated from open heart surgery and various complications associated with the surgery. He never wavered in his support for me, and I will be forever grateful. He is truly a man among men.

Ten percent of the profits from this book will be contributed to the Ardy Sixkiller Clarke Scholarship fund at Montana State University.

BIBLIOGRAPHY

Aronson, Virginia, "John Hunter Gray," *Celestial Healing*, http://celestialhealingstories.com/healings.html.

Beckley, Timothy Green and Sean Casteel, *UFOs Wicked This Way Comes: The Dark Side Of The Ultra-Terrestrials*, Inner Light Global Communications, 2013.

Boylan, Richard, *The Human - Star Nations Connection: Key to History, Current Secrets, and our Near Future*, Richard Boylan, Ph.D., LLC; First edition, 2012.

Brinsley Le Poer Trench, *The Sky People*, Saucerian Books; First edition, 1960.

Bryan, C. D. B. Close Encounters of the Fourth Kind: Alien Abduction, UFOs, and the Conference at M.I.T. Knopf, 1995.

Bullard, Thomas E., "The Rarer Abduction Episodes" in Pritchard, Andrea & Pritchard, David E. & Mack, John E. & Kasey, Pam & Yapp, Claudia. *Alien Discussions: Proceedings of the Abduction Study Conference.* Cambridge: North Cambridge Press, 1994.

Carpenter, John. "Abduction Notes: Reptilians and Other Unmentionables, Part 1," *Alien Jigsaw*, http://alienjigsaw. com/et-contact/Carpenter-Abductions-Reptilians-Nordics. html

Carpenter, John. "The Reality of the Abduction Phenomenon," *MUFON UFO Journal*, 1992.

Cazeau, Charles J., & Stuart D. Scott Jr., *Exploring the Unknown: Great Mysteries Reexamined,* Da Capo Press, 1980.

Clark, Jerome, "The Extraterrestrial Hypothesis in the Early UFO Age" in David M. Jacobs, editor, *UFOs and Abductions: Challenging the Borders of Knowledge,* University Press of Kansas, (pp. 122–140), 2000.

Clark, Ella E. and Margo Edmonds, *Voices of the Winds: Native American Legends,* Castle Books, 2003

Clark, Arthur C., *A Space Odyssey,* Ace. 1993.

Clark News & Media Relations, "Goddard launches space age with historic first 85 years ago today," Clark University, http://www.clarku.edu/article/goddard-launches-space-age-historic-first-85-years-ago-today.

Clemmer, Richard O., "Then You Will Rise and Strike my Head from my Neck: Hopi Prophecy and the Discourse of Empowerment," *American Indian Quarterly* 19:31–73, 1995.

Collyns, Robin, *Did Spacemen Colonize the Earth?,* Regnery, 1976.

Dennett, Preston, UFO Healings, Wildflower Press, 1996.

Frel, Jan, "Inside the Great Reptilian Conspiracy: From Queen Elizabeth to Barack Obama–They Live!", *AlterNet,* 2010.

Garber, Steve, "Sputnik and The Dawn of the Space Age," *NASA.* https://history.nasa.gov/sputnik/

Gibbons, Gavin, *They Rode in Space Ships,* The Citadel Press, 1957.

Hamilton, Ross. *A Tradition of Giants: The Elite Social Hierarchy of American Prehistory.* 2007.

Hancock, Graham, *Fingerprints of the Gods,* Mandarin, 1996.

Hopkins, Budd and Carol Rainey, *Sight Unseen: Science, UFO Invisibility, and Transgenic Beings,* Atria, 2003.

Hopkins, Budd, *Intruders,* Random House, 1987.

Icke, David, *Children of the Matrix: How an Interdimensional Race has Controlled the World for Thousands of Years-and Still Does,* Bridge of Love, 2001.

Jacobs, David, *Walking Among Us: The Alien Plan to Control Humanity,* Disinformation Books, 2015.

Lewis, James R., Editor, *UFOs and Popular Culture,* ABC-CLIO, Inc., 2000.

Mack, John E., *Passport to the Cosmos: Human Transformation and Alien Encounters.* Crown Publishers, 1999.

Mack, John. E. *Abduction Humans Encounters with Aliens* (Revised Edition), Ballantine Books, 1995.

Mackenzie, Donald A., *Pre-Columbian America: Myths and Legends,* Senate, 1996.

McDougall, Walter A., "Shooting the Moon," *American Heritage,* 2010.

Menger, Howard, *From Outer Space to You,* CreateSpace, 2014.

Mills, Kenneth, R., *Colonial Spanish America: A Documentary History,* Rowman & Littlefield, 1998.

Morning Sky, Robert, *The Terra Papers,* Terra, 1980.

"Police Officer Herbert Schirmer Abduction," *UFO Evidence,* December 3, 1967.

Randle, Kevin, *The UFO Casebook,* Grand Central Publishing, 1989.

Reed, A.W., *Aboriginal Myths, Legends, and Fables*, New Holland Publishers, 1999.

Roth, Christopher F., "Ufology as Anthropology: Race, Extraterrestrials, and the Occult" in Debbora Battaglia, editor, *E.T. Culture: Anthropology in Outerspaces*, Duke University Press, 2005.

Schefter, James, *The Race: The Uncensored Story of How America Beat Russia to the Moon*, Doubleday, *1999*.

Shapiro, Joshua, "Star Knowledge UFO Conference Update." *Contact Forum* 4, no. 5 (September–October), 1996.

Sitchin, Zechariah, *The Twelfth Planet*, Avon Books,1976.

Sitchin, Zechariah, *The Wars of Gods and Men*, Avon Books, 1985.

Sitchin, Zechariah. 1990. *Genesis Revisited: Is Modern Science Catching Up with Ancient Knowledge?* Avon Books.

Sitchin, Zechariah. 1993. *When Time Began: The First New Age.* Avon Books, 1993.

Sitchin, Zechariah, *Divine Encounters: A Guide to Visions, Angels, and Other Emissaries*, Avon Books, 1995.

Standing Elk, "Rods on the Yankton." *Contact Forum* 5, no. 3 (May/June): 1997.

Steiger, Brad, *Out of the Dark: The Complete Guide to Beings from Beyond*, Kensington, 2001.

Story, Ronald, *Guardians of the Universe?*, St. Martin's Press, 1980.

Strieber, Whitley, *Communion, A True Story*, Beech Tree Books, 1989.

Summers, Marshall Vian. "The Allies of Humanity Book One,

Sixth Briefing: Questions and Answers," *The Allies of Humanity*, http://alliesofhumanity.org/.

Summers, Marshall Vian, "The Great Waves Prophecy," *The New Message from God*, https://www.newmessage.org/the-message/volume-4/great-waves-change/the-great-waves-prophecy.

Summers, Marshall Vian, "The Tools of the Intervention," *The Allies of Humanity*, http://alliesofhumanity.org/alien-intervention.

Sutherland, Mary, *The Blue People*, http://www.burlingtonnews.net/bluepeople, 2004.

Swerdlow, Stewart, *True World History: Humanity's Saga*, Expansions Publishing, 2014.

"Testament for Believers," *Time*, November 18, 1966.

Tiger Tiger, "Space Age Indian," Album: *Space Age Indian*, TTM Records, 1994.

Trompf, Garry W.; Bernauer, Lauren, "Producing Lost Civilisations: Theosophical Concepts in Literature, Visual Media and Popular Culture" in Cusack, Carole; Norman, Alex. *Handbook of New Religions and Cultural Production*, Brill, 2012.

Temple, Robert, *The Sirius Mystery*, St. Martin's Press, 1976.

Trench, Brinsley Le Poer, *Mysterious Visitors: The UFO Story*, Stein and Day Publishers, 1971.

Vallee, Jacques, *Passport to Magonia: From Folklore to Flying Saucers*, Regnery, 1969.

Wright, Dan. "Commonalities and Disparities: Findings of the MUFON Abduction Transcription Project." MUFON

International UFO Symposium Proceedings, 1995.

Walton, Travis, *Fire in the Sky*, DaCapo Press, 1997.

Ywahoo, Dhyani, *Voices of Our Ancestors: Cherokee Teachings from the Wisdom Fire*, Shambhala Press, 1987.

ABOUT THE AUTHOR

Dr. Ardy Sixkiller Clarke brings to the field of ufology degrees in history, English, psychology, and educational leadership as well as a background as a teacher, university professor, junior college and university administrator, licensed therapist and psychologist, and social science researcher. As a Professor Emeritus at Montana State University and former Director of the Center for Bilingual/ Multicultural Education, Dr. Clarke has worked with indigenous people for most of her career. Her three previous books in the field of ufology are *Encounters with Star People: Untold Stories of American Indians (Anomalist Books)*, *Sky People: Untold Stories of Alien Encounters in Mesoamerica* (New Page Books), and *More Encounters with Star People: Urban American Indians Tell Their Stories* (Anomalist Books). She is also the author of many children's books and the best-selling academic text: *Sisters in the Blood: The Education of Women in Native America*.

She lives in the middle of the Rocky Mountains in Montana with her husband. Her website: www.sixkiller.com provides the latest information on her appearances and writing. You may contact her at: ardy@sixkiller.com.

Printed in November 2021
by Rotomail Italia S.p.A., Vignate (MI) - Italy